Whole Food for Horses

Tigger Montague

Published by BookLocker.com, Inc., St. Petersburg, Florida.

Printed on acid-free paper.

BookLocker.com, Inc.
2016

First Edition

DISCLAIMER

This book details the author's personal experiences with and opinions about whole food ingredients for horses.

The author and publisher are providing this book and its contents on an "as is" basis and make no representations or warranties of any kind with respect to this book or its contents. The author and publisher disclaim all such representations and warranties, including for example warranties of merchantability and healthcare for a particular purpose. In addition, the author and publisher do not represent or warrant that the information accessible via this book is accurate, complete or current.

Except as specifically stated in this book, neither the author or publisher, nor any authors, contributors, or other representatives will be liable for damages arising out of or in connection with the use of this book. This is a comprehensive limitation of liability that applies to all damages of any kind, including (without limitation) compensatory; direct, indirect or consequential damages; loss of data, income or profit; loss of or damage to property and claims of third parties.

You understand that this book is not intended as a substitute for consultation with a licensed healthcare practitioner, such as your veterinarian.

This book provides content related to topics physical and/or mental health issues. As such, use of this book implies your acceptance of this disclaimer.

For my father, Ted Montague, the ultimate foodie, whose love of horses, adventure, and real food gave me the backbone to follow my heart.

Table of Contents

Preface

*"We all eat, and it would be a sad waste of opportunity
to eat badly."*

– Anna Thomas

This book would not be possible without the inspiration and teachings from many horses I have had the privilege to know and learn from. In particular, I'm thinking of a Hanoverian gelding named Lionheart who, like so many horses, is the proverbial "canary in the coal mine." Lionheart was always challenging to keep healthy and sound, and it was he who showed me the path less traveled—an unconventional path that opened my listening and got me out of the box.

Lionheart and I have been together since he was four years old. He has always been a quirky horse, sensitive to touch and to sound, over-reactive, extremely protective of his personal space. Yet he tolerated my shortcomings as a human, despite the times I didn't listen to him, the times I didn't pay attention to what he was trying to tell me.

He was a horse whose medication and vet bills resembled the national debt. No surgeries or major medical problems—just nagging, chronic GI tract issues, lameness, anxiety, and pain. He would improve, and then be not quite right again. His tantrums were legendary and he would simply shut down. And yet when he was feeling good, and he was coming through his body, he was amazing to ride.

Now at age 29, after ten years of eating whole food, his vet bills have been limited to a single bout of uveitis two years ago. Once again he was my teacher; after 48 hours of treatment, the eye had not improved and he seemed to be telling me we were missing a crucial component. So I added bovine colostrum to his feed for immune support and 24 hours later, with the ongoing medications, his eye had improved and went on to fully recover. He hasn't had a relapse since.

This book is not about my company, BioStar, or our products. It is about food, and how feeding horses with real food can make a profound difference in a horse's life in terms of health, performance, welfare, and wellbeing. It is about the choices we make in a challenging global food system, and how those choices affect our animals, families, and Mother Earth.

Everything is connected.

Introduction

Making a switch from commercial equine food products and processed feed can seem daunting at first, and it's no surprise. Commercial feed companies have somehow instilled the horse community with the strange idea that we—owners, riders, trainers, barn managers—can't provide an adequately balanced feed program without their products, because equine nutrition is a subject too complicated for us to understand. It's too bad that we've gotten this idea, for a couple of reasons. For one thing, it's simply not true! For thousands of years, our 'nutritionally uneducated' ancestors managed to help domesticated horses thrive in a world without processed food and synthetic additives. We can still accomplish this today (even if we're somewhat out of practice), because nutrition for horses is the same as it ever was.

The equine diet is, in its most fundamental essence, fiber, protein, fats, carbohydrates, vitamins, minerals and enzymes.

How many of these essential nutritional components are found *only* in processed commercial feed? None. In fact, some of the most beneficial enzymes found in real, unprocessed food are completely missing from commercial feed. All of these components are present in whole-food sources that we can easily find and feed our animals. Remember, as recently as the 1800s, horses were fed what was readily available: pumpkin, squash, cucumbers, turnips, carrots, grains, and a range of native grasses and plants. For these equines, healthy variety really was the spice of life! It's possible that today, even the

1

feed companies have forgotten the sense of satisfaction and well-being that horses once got from eating real grains, vegetables and fruits.

This book is about reclaiming the importance of real food.

Where's the Food?

One summer afternoon in 2008, I put on my reading glasses and walked into the feed room to conduct a little research. Like most horse owners, I trusted the feed companies that I purchased from. I believed their R&D departments full of Ph.D. nutritionists, the marketing of their science, and their repetitive messaging that horse owners are not capable of feeding their own horses without either commercial feeds or an advanced degree in equine nutrition.

The only part of a feed label I had ever paid attention to before was the "guaranteed analysis" part; specifically, I studied the protein, fat, and mineral ratios. I didn't pay so much attention to fiber content, since I figured that with hay and pasture, the horses had plenty of fiber in their diets. Most of my feed-buying decisions simply focused on the percentage of protein and the percentage of fat listed on the label.

This particular afternoon, in the feed room, I pushed my reading glasses up the bridge of my nose and started reading the actual ingredients:

> *...processed grain by-products, roughage products, grain products, plant protein products, molasses products, forage products, soybean oil, calcium carbonate, lignin sulfonate, salt, L-lysine, DL-methionine, vitamin E supplement, iron oxide, anise flavor, fenugreek flavor, choline chloride, copper sulfate, zinc oxide, vitamin B12 supplement, riboflavin supplement, calcium pantothenate, niacin supplement, vitamin A supplement, calcium iodate, magnesium oxide, cobalt*

carbonate, vitamin D3 supplement, ferrous carbonate, manganous oxide, sodium selenite...

The first words out of my mouth: "Where's the *food*?"

I read the label again, thinking surely I had missed something...but no. This nationally known brand had no real food in their feed. I remembered what feed used to look like— whole oats, barley, corn, sometimes mixed with molasses—and the feed mills, the sweet smell of oats in burlap sack bags. No fancy names, no million-dollar marketing campaigns. I wandered back out of the feed room and into the bright sunshine with that woozy, sick feeling, thinking, *Now that I know, how can I feed this? And what would I feed instead?*

The Search

Surely there had to be a commercial feed option out there that provided whole, real food. I knew I would have to compromise on some ingredients, like the inorganic forms of certain minerals—the oxides and carbonates—and I knew I would have to break from my whole food paradigm on vitamins, settling for those made from and processed with petroleum extracts, coal tar, and acetate. But about all the rest of the ingredients, I was hopeful.

I started roaming feed stores like an industrial spy, jotting down ingredients in a notepad, puzzling over some that I couldn't even pronounce: *ethylenediamine dihydroiodide, menadione sodium bisulfite complex, and sodium sesquicarbonate.* All I needed was a secret decoder ring. At least, in the stores, the labels were there to read. When I searched online and visited corporate websites to seek out whole food feeds, I commonly ran into the strange resistance of companies that were unwilling to list their ingredients at all. What were they afraid of?

Around this time, I stumbled across an old, recently reprinted volume called *The Stable Book: A Treatise on the Management of Horses*, written by veterinarian John Stewart and first published in 1858. Stewart's chapters on feeding horses outlined the different ingredients fed around the world at the time: rye bread in Germany, potatoes in Ireland, turnips in England, pumpkin and squash in the U.S., dates and camel milk in Arabia, and fish in India. His feeding recommendations were focused on the amount of work a horse did, and ranged from cavalry horses to cart horses to carriage horses. All of it was just as fascinating as it was potentially useful, even 150 years later.

I recognized that I needed to put together my own whole food feed plan.

So, in my quest for home-made whole-food feed, I started at square one: fiber. I used beet pulp as a base. (Note that this was before genetically modified sugar beets took over the market— more on that development later.) Next, I added oats for protein and carbohydrate energy, flax seeds for omega-3 fatty acids and other fats, and soaked alfalfa cubes for additional protein, fiber, and calcium. All of this I rounded out with some brewer's yeast for the B-vitamins, spirulina for the macro- and microminerals, and sunflower seeds for vitamin E.

The horses loved it. And within a few weeks of eating this new diet, they looked better. Even though they had looked fine on the commercial complete feed, something profound had happened internally. Much later, I would come to understand that feeding a simple whole food diet puts less stress on the GI tract and the body system at large.

Over time, I experimented with other food ingredients: low-arsenic rice bran, barley, timothy pellets, chia seeds, coconut meal, coconut oil, hemp oil and seeds, and ground almonds, along with various foods I could mix in to give more variety, like kale, oranges, kiwis, papaya, strawberries, blueberries, mangos, pomegranates, and cabbage. Many of BioStar's first formulas were born from testing each ingredient on my herd at home. One of the greatest advantages to feeding a whole food diet, is that it allows for full customization—a kind of mindfulness about feeding. It allows us to adjust quantities based on the caloric and energy needs of each horse, and it can be adjusted to the metabolism of each individual animal.

I could have easily called my approach "Our Ancestors' Diet for Horses," but instead I called it "The Whole Food Diet," because I felt it was so important to distinctly separate this diet from commercial, convenient, processed feeds. Feeding horses does not require advanced degrees in nutrition, and never has. The cornerstones of the equine diet are fiber, protein, carbohydrates and fat, just the same as they were in our ancestors' day, and the best way to supply these four elements of nutrition is with good hay, pasture, and real food.

Commercial Processed Feed:
The Good, the Bad, and the Ugly

There is no question that commercially processed horse feed has, for many decades, provided considerable convenience to horse and barn owners. It doesn't get much easier than ripping open commercial processed feed bags, scooping out pellets, sweet feed or texturized feed, and pouring it in the bucket. Since commercially processed horse feed is, by and large, a "complete" feed, these formulas help make feeding less complicated, taking out the guesswork, and in many cases reducing the need for additional multivitamin/mineral supplementation. Many of the feed companies do, in fact, advise that there is no need to add anything further in the way of vitamins and minerals to their complete feed formulas. In addition, these companies typically provide many different feed formulas, thus providing horse owners with some degree of choice when matching a commercial feed diet to a particular horse. All of this translates into considerably less time and energy spent by owners to ensure that their horses are fed at least adequately.

Without a doubt, "complete" commercial feeds have offered significant time savings and convenience in our daily lives ever since they were first marketed. Since then, however, we've learned a lot more about the real price of these benefits. What was once hoped to be a perfect way for providing total nutrition with total convenience has led us to the central paradox we face today:

Convenience and nutrition are deeply at odds with each other.

To understand why this is, we can look back to the beginnings of commercial feed. The more I learned in my earlier days of studying equine nutrition, the more I wondered how the processed food revolution started in the first place—not just for horses, but for humans too. So, during one of my frequent trips down the research rabbit hole, I took a look at the early history of one huge U.S. commercial producer of "people feed."

Like Purina, the Kellogg Company had an ambition to make products that were nutritious *and* highly convenient. When that company's first whole grain cereals became so successful in the early 1900s, a problem arose along with it. Fulfilling high demand meant maintaining centralized warehouses full of product, which meant that the product needed the shelf life to accommodate this type of storage. Kellogg's Corn Flakes, which were roasted, still kept a percentage of oil, which caused the flakes to go rancid within only a few weeks after packaging. So, in 1905, Kellogg made a huge compromise; they altered their production method to eliminate the corn germ and the bran, using only the starchy center of the corn. Unbeknownst to Kellogg at the time, the bran and germ contained many vitamins and other phytonutrients which, many years later, would be added back to the flakes in the inexpensive forms of synthetic, coal tar and/or petrochemical derivatives—a replacement strategy that works in theory but not so well in practice, as we'll soon find out.

Thus began the common practice of choosing greater convenience—of production, storage, pricing, purchasing, consuming—over the high-caliber nutrition that simply isn't possible when food products are mass-manufactured in cheap and easy ways. In 1904, the Quaker Oats Company introduced a new technology called "gun puffing." The method was demonstrated at the World's Fair in St. Louis using army surplus canons which were crammed full of white rice and then heated. As the cannons got hot, pressure increased inside the chambers, and when the chambers opened, the resulting sudden drop in pressure forced the rice to explode. Soon after gun-puffed grains eventually became popular, along came extrusion machines in the 1930s. These devices could (and still do) take multiple ingredients and mix them together rapidly to form an endless array of shapes and sizes. As author Melanie Warner (Pandora's Lunchbox, 2013) writes:

> *Extrusion is undoubtedly the harshest and most nutritionally devastating way to process. These are not gentle machines. They look a bit like oversized jackhammers turned on their sides. Inside the long, steel barrel the starch, sugar, and protein molecules are ripped apart by twisting screws that generate large amounts of heat and pressure. Think of extrusion as a molecular melting pot...The process is referred to as "plasticisation", which neatly sums up the nutritional gist of what happens inside an extruder.*

Let's look a little closer at what kind of treatment Warner is talking about. To create the thick, homogenized slurry that goes into the extruder, the ingredients are first ground and steam-cooked under pressure, then dried and toasted. In the process, grain and other raw materials can be subjected to temperatures over 600°F—hot enough to effectively kill off all the naturally occurring B-vitamins, vitamin C, vitamin A, vitamin E, folate, and phytonutrients these grains had to offer. Replacement vitamins and minerals, along with sweeteners, are typically coated onto the flakes during the toasting procedure.

We find a very similar situation in the equine feed industry, where either extrusion or pelletizing is used. The pelletizing method for processed feed requires that food ingredients (grains, forages, etc.) be ground or compressed in a roll-and-die assembly (think of a hammermill) which reduces the average particle size. Pelletizing also requires heating before the mix is forced through holes in the mill and cooled. As with the extrusion process, replacement vitamin and mineral pre-mixes are commonly sprayed onto the pellets afterward. Although the feed companies' pelletizing process isn't quite as brutal to food as extrusion, it does allow for lower-quality raw materials because the consumer can't "see" into the pellets. Texturized feeds (think granola) use more whole grain, but may incorporate pellets for the vitamin and mineral pre-mixes.

In this journey of learning more about the history of processed feed (and processed food for humans), I ran across a pioneer consumer activist: Harvey W. Wiley, who waged a 50-year crusade for pure foods. Starting in 1883, as chief chemist at the fairly new U.S. Department of Agriculture, Wiley tried half a dozen times to introduce the nation's first pure food legislation. In 1902, an official from a large food distribution company told Congress that Wiley's bill would actually ruin all sectors of the food industry simply by requiring honesty in manufacturing and labeling. "Make us leave preservatives and coloring matters out of our food, and make us call products by their right name," he warned, "and you will have bankrupted every food industry in the country."

Wiley fought against concentrated sweeteners such as corn syrup, and wanted additives and other non-traditional chemical ingredients identified clearly on food packages. Interestingly enough, he fought Monsanto's inaugural product: saccharin. He considered saccharin (a.k.a. benzoic sulfimide) potentially harmful to the kidneys, and felt that adding it to canned foods was at best a deceitful quality-compromising practice, and at worst unsafe. In 1914, it was Wiley who offered this straightforward, now-famous quote to *Good Housekeeping* magazine: "I have always stood for food that is food."

That was over 100 years ago! One can only imagine what Wiley would think of today's current array of adulterated food and processed feed.

Diet and DNA

When it comes to changes in how we process food and feed for human and animal consumption, the 21st century has ushered in an entirely new set of concerns. Since 1997, genetically engineered (GE) and genetically modified organism (GMO) versions of corn and soy have been widely used in commercially processed horse feed. While the scientific community continues to debate the safety of GE and GMO food, one undeniable effect is already here: the greatly increased amount of pesticides and herbicides used in the growing of these new plants. Because some of these crops have an herbicide-tolerance gene inserted, one predictable consequence has been that the weeds for which farmers are spraying have "reacted" by simply becoming more herbicide resistant—resulting in still more herbicide and pesticide use, compounding the original problem and further toxifying the environment. Additionally, GM crops also degrade healthy levels of seed diversity and intensify existing soil erosion problems. Real and potential problems are many, and whatever the scientific community ultimately concludes about GE and GMO crops, a solid bottom line is already taking shape: feed formulas that use corn and or soy (and are not clearly marked as GE-free or GMO-free) do not lead us toward a greener, more eco-friendly environment.

Modern food and feed processing: More is less?

Whether genetically modified or not, today most of our grains (corn, soy, oats, wheat) are funneled into commercial channels for processing—unlike in countries such as Canada and some of the EU nations, where there's more reliance on a system of local feed mills, or where grains are sold directly from the farm to other farmers for livestock feed. The advantage of a local feed mill/farmer arrangement is in the quality of grains over mere quantity (and the reduction in fossil fuel consumption for long distance shipping to processing facilities). The U.S., however, has followed essentially the same food/feed production path it has been on since high-volume commercial processing began in earnest over 100 years ago. More than ever, the emphasis is on quantity over quality, convenience over nutrition.

At the processing plants, grains are sorted and graded, with the superior grains going to human consumption and lower-rated grains going to animal consumption. Byproducts of processing (for example, soy hulls and wheat middlings) become cheap fillers for horse feed. Because the grains for animals are nutritionally poorer than the human-grade grains, processed horse feed companies must still add vitamins and nutrients via synthetic additives made from coal tar derivatives, petroleum extracts, acetone, formaldehyde and even, in the case of vitamin D, irradiated cattle brains. The processing of the grains themselves can expose them to temperatures exceeding 450 degrees—well above the 145-degree maximum over which enzymes, along with certain vitamins and other important phytonutrients, can't survive.

The high fructose corn syrup used to sweeten commercially processed animal feed can contain as much as 80% fructose and only 20% glucose. In natural fruit, the ratio is usually 50% glucose and 50% fructose. Moreover, unadulterated fruit contains fiber which slows down the metabolism of fructose and other sugars. In contrast, the fructose in processed high-fructose corn syrup is absorbed very quickly in the horse's (or human's) GI tract.

Another note on sweeteners: sugar, in the form of molasses, is often added to horse feeds as a binder and for palatability. Molasses is made from sugar cane, with sulfur dioxide used during processing to lighten the color, help extend its shelf life, and as a processing aid when the cane has been harvested at an early stage. Trouble is, you may also recognize sulfur dioxide as a primary component of acid rain, and a pollutant of enormous concern to environmental scientists.

But toxicity issues aside for a moment, look at some of what we're already losing from food by subjecting it to these harsh, high-temperature processing methods: natural enzymes, important vitamins and phytonutrients, and sugars in their natrual ratios and digestible forms. When we take into account what happens in the later processing steps—the addition of synthetically derived nutrient replacements, along with an array of sweeteners, additives and preservatives (which we'll discuss in a moment) to produce pelletized, extruded and/or texturized horse feeds—it becomes clear that a major transformation has taken place. What was once food is now "food product". By looking at it all in these terms, we can start to understand the true price of convenience.

Preservatives

I once gave a seminar in Wellington, Florida, where several questions were raised in the audience about certain preservatives in horse feed and supplements. At the time, I didn't know much about them; my company didn't use them then, and we still don't. But I knew that added preservatives were out there in force, so I decided to hop down into the research rabbit hole and educate myself. Here's some of what I learned, and think you should know too, about the preservatives commonly used in commercial equine feed formulations:

Ethoxyquin was developed over 35 years ago as a rubber stabilizer by Monsanto. Approved as a both a fungicide and a horse feed preservative, ethoxyquin is used in feeds to protect fats from rancidity (lipid peroxidation). The chemical foundation of ethoxyquin is quinoline, which is made from coal tar (just like the B-vitamins found in pet supplements, human supplements, and equine supplements). Quinoline is also the foundation for an herbicide called Assert® (Canadian trade name Spike-Up®) and as a growth-regulator fungicide used to protect apples and pears during harvest and storage.

In the 1990s, the U.S. Food and Drug Administration's Center for Veterinary Medicine investigated reports that ethoxyquin in dog food was linked with a "myriad of adverse effects, such as allergic reactions, skin problems, major organ failure, behavior problems, and cancer."

Propionic acid is formed synthetically from ethyl alcohol and carbon monoxide. It is classified by the EPA as a fungicide and bactericide. BASF is the world's largest manufacturer of propionic acid, producing 149,000 metric tons in 2010. Propionic acid is found in apple cider vinegar (along with lactic, citric, and acetic acids) and is also a chemical component of human sweat. However, the form used in feeds and hay is not from apple cider vinegar; it is the synthetic form. The New Jersey Department of Health has indicated that the synthetic form of propionic acid is a carcinogen, with perhaps the greatest danger appearing when it is used it to spray crops. I could find no data at all about the dangers of propionic acid to horses, though it is routinely used on hay in various parts of the country. For now, it appears to be relatively safe for equine ingestion, but more research is needed.

Citric acid is a component of citrus fruits, although the version used as a horse feed preservative is not extracted from lemons, oranges, and limes; it is made through the fermentation of corn-steep liquor, molasses, and hydrolyzed corn starch. At the end of the fermentation process, citric acid is isolated by precipitating it with calcium hydroxide to yield calcium citrate salt that is then regenerated with sulfuric acid. The corn byproducts used (corn-steep liquor, and hydrolyzed corn starch) are from genetically modified corn. In 2007, worldwide annual production of citric acid stood at 1.6 million tons, with China the largest producer nationally, manufacturing over half the world's supply. In the U.S., Archer Daniels Midland is the largest commercial producer.

Very little is known about potential equine sensitivities to citric acid or the byproducts of its extraction process. However, humans who are sensitive to MSG (monosodium glutamate) should be aware that during citric acid processing, not all of the corn protein is removed—resulting in hydrolyzed protein which then yields free glutamic acid (MSG). Individuals with MSG sensitivities should know that textured protein, soy protein, soy protein concentrate, soy protein isolate, whey protein, whey protein concentrate, whey protein isolate, and citric acid always contain this processed free glutamic acid.

Antibiotics are medicine, not food

Distillers grains, also known as "distillers dried grains with solubles," are a common ingredient in processed feeds. As the name implies, these are a byproduct of the distillation process, which for the longest time I had assumed was nothing more than the "leftovers" of beer and spirit distilleries. Then a 2012 story in *Wired Science* (followed two days later by an article in the *Washington Post*) brought the reality of distillers dried grains to my full attention.

Distillers grains are a byproduct of the manufacture of ethanol (a.k.a. ethyl alcohol), with the massive amounts of GMO corn in the U.S. grown, in part, to support that industry. Making ethanol is a lot like brewing beer: you take a starchy carbohydrate (corn), wet it down to make a mash, warm it up, and add yeast. Unfortunately, it is common for the mash to become contaminated with bacteria such as *Lactobacillus*, which compete with the yeast for the sugars in the mash. Instead of producing alcohol, however, these bacteria leave behind lactic acid. This lowers the ethanol yield, so ethanol producers solve this problem by infusing the mash with—that's right—antibiotics.

For mashes, the most commonly used antimicrobial drugs are penicillin, virginiamycin, erythromycin, tylosin and tetracycline. After fermentation is complete and the ethanol yield has been obtained, the leftover mash is conveniently sold for use in feeds for horses, swine, cattle, and chickens. In fact, distillers grains have proven to be quite an economic boon to the ethanol producers. The question is, how much antibiotic residue eventually makes it into bags of feed?

In 2008, the FDA tested 45 dried distillers grains samples, 24 of which came back positive. Fifteen of the samples (33 percent) contained residues of virginiamycin; 12 samples (27 percent) contained residues of erythromycin, and five samples (11 percent) contained tylosin. According to the FDA, "Some were detected at levels considered significant, including residue levels exceeding 0.5 ppm." In another study conducted by the University of Minnesota, samples of dried distillers grains were collected from various ethanol manufacturing plants quarterly over a one-year period and analyzed for antibiotic residue. All 117 samples tested contained antibiotic residue.

Most of the news and uproar in recent years has been about antibiotic overuse as it relates to humans. But in 2012, with an estimated 80 percent of all antibiotics sold in the U.S. ending up on animal farms, it became clear that more attention was needed here as well. In April of that year, the FDA released a statement that called on drug companies to help limit the use of antibiotics in farm animals, which scientists concluded had been contributing to a surge in drug-resistant bacteria. Under the new FDA guidelines, antibiotics for animals are to be used "judiciously" and only when necessary. The World Health Organization and the Institute of Medicine, among others, have called the waning effectiveness of antibiotics a global health concern. Still, the National Pork Producers Council, in response to the FDA's request that drug companies voluntarily limit antibiotic use, stated that "the FDA did not provide compelling evidence that antibiotic use in livestock is unsafe."

I mention this quote from the National Pork Producers Council to highlight the challenges now inherent to factory farming; too many animals in confined spaces means increased disease risk to those animals, leading to the widespread use of antibiotics on factory farms we see today. Given this status quo, it's little surprise that these farms want to continue with business as usual, despite requests from the FDA to reduce antibiotic use.

How are our horses affected?

In terms of the equine community, there have been no studies conducted yet on levels of antibiotic residue in horses from dried distillers grains. At this point we don't even know how biologically active or passive these residues are, and we know very little about how antibiotic residue may affect our horses over time. However, the FDA has clearly stated its concern that antibiotic residues in distillers grains could be transferred to animal tissue upon ingestion. Meanwhile, there *is* some encouraging news on the alternative methods front. Some ethanol manufacturing plants have begun to use extracts from hops (yes, the beer-making herb, which has natural antibiotic properties), while other ethanol producers have started to use stabilized chlorine dioxide to combat bacterial growth, eliminating the use of antibiotics altogether.

Hopefully, alternative methods of inhibiting bacteria during ethanol production are a real trend. At present, though, there is no way to know if dried distillers grains are antibiotic-free or not simply by reading an equine feed or supplement label. As of early 2016, no commercial feed company has come forward to announce that their products are antibiotic-free. Maybe they all are, maybe some of them are, maybe none of them are. In September, 2011, one ethanol producer who markets distillers grains under the name "Dakota Gold" did announce that its offerings were now antibiotic-free, as reported in a cattle feed industry publication. Here's to hoping that other suppliers follow suit.

What's a consumer to do?

Remember that we are not powerless against these suspect ingredients in equine feed and supplements. We can vote with our pocketbooks. We can demand from the feed companies that they provide documentation of antibiotic-free distillers grains, and we can demand the same from supplement companies that use distillers grains in their products. And, of course, we can just stop buying any feed or supplement that contains distillers grains that are not labeled "antibiotic-free".

Keep in mind also that these distillers grains and solubles are fed to chickens, swine, and cattle too. Which means that if you're a meat-eater who shops at the grocery store for conventional meat (i.e., not organic and not labeled antibiotic-free"), the residual antibiotics are most likely going to be in the meat you and your family eats—contributing, over time, to the development of antibiotic-resistant bacterial strains.

Bottom line: Antibiotics are important in the ongoing fight against harmful and deadly bacteria. To my mind, they need not be in food.

Diluted food and the flavoring "fix"

It's difficult to find a bag of feed or even a supplement that doesn't list "natural and artificial flavorings" among its ingredients. Part of the answer to why this is, can be found in the agricultural revolution that began after World War II. The impetus to grow more food meant that how the food actually tasted was not as important as growing a *lot* of food. It was quantity over quality. New hybrid seeds plus an arsenal of fertilizers meant that farmers could produce more per acre...resulting in more food, yes, but less taste and, in the words of one famous chef, "blandness." That blandness, in part, comes from lower nutritional content, higher carbohydrate content, and greater moisture content of the food. There's even a term for this: dilution.

Not only is the food that humans eat bland, so are the feeds and concentrates and supplements that horses, dogs, cattle, pigs, goats, sheep, and chickens eat. Animals and humans are less inclined to eat bland food, so flavorings are added to stimulate smell and taste. Flavoring chemicals give food specific smells that the food industry calls "flavor". The same mixture of chemicals would be called "fragrance" if added to cleaning products, perfumes or personal care products. *Smell makes up to 80 percent of the sense of taste.* If something smells good to a horse, dog, or human, our brains think it will taste good too. By the way, there are taste receptors in the GI tract, too—sensors for fat, protein, bacteria, hormones and plant compounds. These receptors play an important role in how humans and animals feel during and after eating.

So what are these flavoring additives? The term "natural flavorings" sounds innocuous enough; perhaps it means a nice apple flavor from a real apple, or carrot flavor from a real carrot? How about delicious real meat juice as a "natural" flavoring in dog food? Not quite. The sad truth is, "natural flavorings" are created in laboratories using hundreds of chemical compounds. To be deemed "natural" by the FDA, only *one* component of a flavoring needs to come from a plant, tree, spice, vegetable, yeast, meat, poultry, egg, or dairy product whose significant function is for flavor, and not nutritional. Flavorings contain solvents, emulsifiers, and preservatives, which can make up the majority of ingredients in each specific flavoring itself. Take apple flavoring for instance; as many as 50 chemicals can be used to approximate the taste of an apple. Other "natural" flavorings can incorporate up to 200 blended chemical additives. Some of the additives you may see on labels include: *propylene glycol, polyglycerol esters of fatty acid, mono and di-glycerides, benzoic acid, polysorbate 80, BHT, and BHA.* According to research by the Environmental Working Group, *"natural and artificial flavors really aren't that different."*

In the livestock business flavorings are often called "palatants", and their purpose is simply to encourage animals to eat more. Much of the feed for animals is made up of the starchy grains—corn, millet, barley—because feeding carbs is cheaper than feeding fats. It has been estimated that as many as 75% of cattle and hogs eat palatants during their lifetimes. Remember, farmers growing animals for food want their animals to get big as fast as possible before going to slaughter. But by increasing the flavor of feed in order to get animals to eat more and thus get bigger and fatter, the ones that aren't killed as youngsters often become obese and susceptible to metabolic disease.

Accounting for taste

What kind of financial stakes are we talking about? The fragrance and flavor industry is estimated to rake in $24 billion annually. This is not a small industry. Its sheer size underscores just how much of our food, our horses' food, and our dogs' food contains flavorings. Perhaps the industry's growth can be better understood in this context: In a 2011 interview on *60 Minutes*, two flavor scientists from the Givaudan corporation (which posted $4.4 billion in revenue for 2014) said that one of their goals was making food "addictive."

Horses and dogs and humans crave variety in food; fake flavors dress up foods that are very similar and make them seem more different than they really are. The technology of fake flavors applied to bland food induces the sense of smell, and tricks the brain into a heightened level of pleasure. Like a person with alcoholism or drug addiction—always needing more in order to get that initial experience of "high" or "bliss"—the more we eat food with flavorings, the more we crave. Author Mark Schatzker's book *The Dorito Effect* highlights why "we can't eat just one Dorito." It's not the corn chip itself, or even the fat it's fried in. It's the taste, coming from a concoction of flavoring chemicals—a kind of opiate for the brain, leading to extra pounds for the body.

Eating processed foods that are addictive in this way leads us to a type of frustration; we chase satiety without ever really reaching it, even at the bottom of the chip bag. When we eat wild blueberries or organic heirloom tomatoes, we tend to eat less and not "pig out" like we do on Big Macs, Chicken McNuggets and soft drinks. This is because real food provides a deeper satiety via the complex of nutritional factors in food, along with one other important component: toxins. Organisms like plants contain small amounts of toxins; for example the tiny amount of cyanide naturally present in apple seeds. One theory is that mammal brains and GI tracts evolved a system to regulate the consumption of toxins. When we eat real food, we become satiated, and the dose of toxins obtained in the food isn't enough to hurt us. As Schatzker says, "Nature has mastered the art of hedonic density—food that maximizes pleasure and minimizes calories." The problem today is that food grown on an industrial scale is far less delicious, while the food that we, our horses, and our dogs should *really* not eat— flavorings, byproducts, highly processed ingredients—is much more exciting to our taste buds than it is to our bodies.

The MSG connection

No discussion of addictive flavoring ingredients is complete without mentioning MSG (monosodium glutamate), a flavor enhancer found in pet foods under the name "hydrolyzed protein" among others. The Association of American Feed Control Officials (AAFCO) allows pet food companies to call it "natural flavors" or "natural flavorings". In equine feeds and supplements, MSG itself may also be labeled as: "protein isolate", "texturized protein", "autolyzed yeast extract", hydrolyzed yeast extract", "soy extract" (or "concentrate"), "glutamate", or simply "natural flavor". Other ingredients that often contain MSG or give rise to MSG during processing, include maltodextrin, carageenan, protease, citric acid, corn starch, gelatin, and pectin. MSG overstimulates the nervous system, and can cause an inflammatory response. Because it can overexcite cells to the point of damage, MSG has been called an *excitotoxin*. There's little doubt that this compound, along with other factors, has contributed to the damage associated with the rise in obesity and metabolic syndrome in humans, dogs and horses. In the last 50 years, as the food has become bland, the rise in flavorings has exploded. So have our waistlines, and the girths of our horses. Today less than one third of Americans are slender, which means two thirds are either overweight or obese. Additionally, a recent survey indicated that 50 percent of American dogs are overweight. MSG and other flavorings aren't the single reason for these issues, of course, but they are a contributing factor. Remember, feeling satiated from real food ultimately means eating less, but getting more nutrition.

In summary: our industrial food system grows food full of carbohydrates and moisture and almost literally no taste. What's more, due to the years of chemical fertilizer and pesticide applications, the soil no longer provides enough nutrients to the plants, so fortification is necessary in the form of synthetic or coal tar-derivative vitamins. In the case of commercial horse feed, the ingredients are from the industrial food complex, and most of these ingredients are not even "whole". They are byproducts: wheat middlings, dried distillers grains (the leftover mash from ethanol production), soybean hulls, wheat flour, corn distillers grains (also from ethanol production), corn germ, de-hulled soybean meal. Because byproducts are even less nutrient-dense than the whole food they were once a part of, nutrient fortification is needed, along with flavoring so that the stuff tastes like something any animal might want to eat.

Undoing the blandness "fix": Getting flavorings out of the diet

Added flavorings are widespread, but they can be avoided by reading the ingredient labels on feed and supplement packages, and keeping a few things in mind:

- Whole food component products like *Cool Stance, Renew Gold*, alfalfa pellets, timothy pellets, whole flax seeds, whole chia seeds, and whole oats do not contain flavorings of any kind. Neither do organic or cold pressed oils like hemp, coconut, camelina and flax.

- Highly processed oils like vegetable, soy, corn, and canola can contain flavorings.

- Most all supplements for horses contain natural or artificial flavorings, and the often-hidden MSG. Remember, it's not just the number of chemical additives in flavorings; it's how those chemicals and the ingredients they are combined with affect, over time, the body system at large, and the GI tract in particular.

- A note on pasture grasses: Pasture seeds are much richer in carbohydrates than native grasses. Currently, seeds for pasture grasses are intended to fatten cattle and produce vast quantities of milk from dairy cows. Grass seed companies want grasses with lower fiber content and higher sugar and fructan content. Hay farmers are encouraged to cut hay in the afternoon when the sugar levels are higher. These factors are going to reduce natural satiation, increasing calorie intake and weight.

- A note on food for dogs: Read the labels! Feed raw if you can, and reduce the amount of kibble by adding whole food like buffalo, venison, salmon, organic chicken and eggs. When dogs eat real food, they maintain a healthier weight.

- A note on food for humans: Buy organic real food, or food from a farmer's market or CSA. Food in a package—even labeled "organic"—can have flavorings added. Even "antibiotic-free" chicken often has added flavorings.

The Whole Food Diet

Whole food: What it is, what it isn't

As we've seen, the labels of most commercial processed feeds feature a lot of additives in the form of synthetic nutrients and inorganic minerals, and not much actual food. There is, of course, *some* food, but it's low-grade and in many cases has been further refined. It's in many ways a reflection of our entire processed food culture, from the original TV dinners of the 1950s, up to our present-day microwave meals and fast foods. Horse feed, which once upon a time consisted simply of whole grains, is now another processed, convenience food product.

To understand what whole food is, it's good to first understand what it isn't. In the early 2000s, Gyorgy Scrinis, a research associate at the Globalism Institute at RMIT University, Melbourne, Australia coined the term **nutritionism** to describe an ideology based on the premise that the nutritional value of any food can be found by simply adding up the values of its individual nutrients. To be clear, the term was first used by Scrinis (and later by like-minded journalist Michael Pollan) in a negative way. They actually regarded nutritionism as a scientifically popular, but highly suspect way of thinking about the roles of nutrients in the foods we eat. The reductionist approach of isolating nutrients from their plant and food sources, then re-creating them in a laboratory is not nutrition: it's nutritionism. Nutrients in food provide a complex of important biological cofactors, including fiber, amino acids, antioxidants, and enzymes which are critical to health and well-being. In fact, the nutritionism mindset is essentially the opposite of the whole food approach to nutrition, and perhaps one that misses the forest for the trees; the roles of individual nutrients are overemphasized and removed from the context of the larger, more complex foods that contain them.

In this way, the nutritionism approach can be seen as a dangerous oversimplification of what we and our animals do and don't need in our diets. Unfortunately, it's also the basis from which many nutritional scientists do their daily work: take a food and study one element at a time to determine *why* the food is healthy, beneficial, fights cancer, etc. As Marion Nestle, a professor of nutrition, food studies and public health at New York University says, "the problem with nutrient-by-nutrient nutrition science is that it takes the nutrient out of the context of food." Scrinis himself elaborates that "instead of worrying about nutrients we need to simply avoid any food that has been processed to such an extent that it is more the product of an industry than of nature."

Whether we're talking about feeding humans or horses, whole food—real, unrefined, intact, complete food—is more than merely the sum of its individual nutrient parts. Throwing a list of ingredients in a bowl doesn't magically create a soufflé, just like mixing a bunch of food-derived material with synthetically isolated vitamins and minerals in a vat doesn't result in real food that we and our animals can use toward real health and well-being.

Why go the whole food route?

- Adopting a whole food diet allows the owner, rider or trainer to custom-feed each horse according to its needs.
- A whole food diet gives full control of any dietary adjustments to the owner, trainer or rider; you're no longer limited by which commercial blends are already available.
- Whole food diets eliminate processed feed elements like wheat middlings, soy, dried distillers grains, and oils processed with hexane.
- A whole food diet does require the addition of a multivitamin/mineral supplement; healthy, minimally processed sources can be chosen instead of resorting to petrochemical industry preparations.

Hay

Horses are biologically designed to eat twenty hours per day. Unlike deer, they are not browsers, they are grazers. Chewing produces saliva, which helps buffer stomach acids. On a pasture/hay diet a horse normally produces up to 10 gallons of saliva per day. When there is less for the horse to eat all day, less saliva is produced which translates into less buffering of the stomach acids. This can result in an increased imbalance of the bacteria in the stomach, and increased production of stomach acid, and thus the potentially elevated chance of gastric ulcers. If the stomach becomes more acidic than it should be, gas is produced by bacterial fermentation, and the result can be pain, colic, or even stomach wall rupture.

If a metabolic or overweight horse fasts for longer than three hours, the adrenal glands release cortisol in reaction to the stress. This causes the body to go into "survival mode," increasing blood sugar levels and storing more fat. The solution for these horses is not to give less hay, but rather to hay more frequently in smaller amounts. Nibble nets are extremely helpful to the metabolic and overweight horses because it takes longer for them to eat a flake of hay. In most training and boarding situations, the most critical time of fasting occurs after midnight, when the horse has finished his late-night hay and now waits five to six hours before morning feed. Nibble nets given at night-check help reduce fasting time.

Protein

Protein provides amino acids for building and maintaining muscle and soft tissue, the synthesis and release of hormones, the synthesis of neurotransmitters and enzymes. It is the predominant component of blood, organs, muscles and enzymes.

Protein makes the horse

Whether we're talking about the fundaments of a whole food equine diet, or actively working to build and maintain a horse's topline, protein plays a crucial structural role in the body. *Eighty percent* of a horse's anatomy is built from proteins. These complex molecules are, in turn, made up of chains of amino acids, which are absorbed from the small intestine. Twenty different amino acids are needed for protein synthesis; however, ten of these amino acids (known as *essential* amino acids) must be supplied to the horse through the diet. These come from quality protein sources like alfalfa, whey, hemp, peas, and eggs that provide all the essential amino acids including lysine and the branched-chain amino acids (BCAAs). Over-processing feeds can reduce the biological value (BV) of the protein, which may not be well absorbed by the horse.

Some feeds and supplements contain soy as a quality protein source, although there are issues to be aware of when using soy as a source of protein for horses: soy phytoestrogens can disrupt endocrine function; almost all the soy used for horses and livestock is genetically modified to withstand being sprayed with glyphosate, the active ingredient in Roundup. According to Monsanto's own research, "Roundup Ready" soybeans contain 29% less choline than conventional soybeans and 27% more trypsin inhibitor— a potential allergen that can

31

interfere with protein digestion. Lectins, which are culprits in soy allergies, are at nearly doubled levels in Roundup Ready soybeans. What's more, one of the leading scientists in plant pathology, Dr. Don Huber, has identified a new pathogen from Roundup exposure that has increased infertility in livestock.

Alfalfa and timothy

Alfalfa has been fed to horses for hundreds of years. It provides all the essential amino acids including lysine and methionine, as well as the nonessential amino acids. It also provides all the BCAAs so important for building and maintaining muscle. Alfalfa hay ranges in protein content from 18 to 26 percent depending on growing conditions, drying conditions, and storage. Alfalfa's high calcium content can help buffer stomach acid without stopping acid production completely, as is the case with proton inhibitors such as omeprazole. Alfalfa pellets and cubes are lower in protein than alfalfa hay (ranging from 15 to 18 percent), yet still maintain the same amino acid profile. The high protein amount in alfalfa hay can make some horses a little too full of themselves; however, the lower protein percentage of cubes and pellets makes alfalfa an excellent base food for a whole-food feed. Alfalfa is high in fiber, coming in at an average of 30 percent, and is the lowest in sugar of the most commonly fed hays: orchard grass and timothy grass.

Timothy pellets or cubes provide lower protein content, ranging from 8 to 10 percent. Like alfalfa, timothy also provides the essential, nonessential, and branched-chain amino acids. It can have a higher non-structural carbohydrate content than alfalfa, as its sugar content is higher on average. Timothy cubes or pellets can be an excellent alternative to alfalfa as a base food for a whole-food feed for horses in light work, and horses that are easy keepers. A blend of timothy and alfalfa pellets or cubes provides a moderate amount of protein, higher calcium, and the benefits of a legume (alfalfa) and a grass (timothy). Variety can help support a wider range of beneficial microorganisms in the GI tract.

Oats and barley

Oats are one of the oldest grains fed to horses. Their protein content ranges from 9 to 12 percent and includes the essential amino acids. Barley is higher in protein coming in at 10 to 13 percent on average, but has a lower amino acid profile than oats. Both these grains are high in non-structural carbohydrates, with oats coming it at 44.4 percent starch and 4.8 percent sugar, and barley coming in at 53 percent starch and 6 percent sugar. Barley provides more quick burn energy from the starches than oats, although horses that don't require more calories for energy may not need either of these grains.

Oats and barley are higher in phosphorus than calcium and need to be balanced with hays like timothy or a timothy/alfalfa mix, or an orchard grass/alfalfa mix that provide more calcium. Mixing timothy or alfalfa pellets/cubes with oats or barley in a 2:1 ratio will balance the calcium/phosphorus minerals.

Understanding whey protein

Whey protein from cows' milk comes in various forms: isolate, concentrate, and hydrolyzed. One of the most bioavailable forms of whey protein is un-denatured whey protein concentrate. This means the whey has undergone minimal processing: single-flash pasteurization that does not require high heat. This method ensures that the active peptides, immunoglobins and serum albumin are intact, as they would be in raw milk. Un-denatured whey protein has twice the amount of individual BCAAs as peas or highly processed whey protein. This is important especially in the case of the amino acid leucine, which plays a vital role in the synthesis of new muscle. If you are feeding your horse a supplement with whey protein, you may want to check with the company to see that the whey comes from cows that are grass fed, r-BGH-free, and antibiotic-free.

Hemp, egg, and pea proteins

These three protein sources provide the essential amino acids including lysine, and the BCAAs. Like other whole food protein sources such as alfalfa they also provide other nutritional components: hemp provides edestin and albumin proteins as well as fiber and key minerals such as zinc and magnesium. Egg protein is high in sulfur-containing amino acids such as methionine, which play a critical role in cell metabolism and protein synthesis. Pasteurized, whole egg protein ensures that biotin will not be depleted. Pea protein is a rich source of arginine, the amino acid that stimulates nitric oxide, and is the precursor of creatine, helping with the maintenance of ATP for more muscle power.

Carbohydrates

Carbohydrates are compounds in foods that can be broken down to release energy in the body. Carbohydrates can be classified into three categories:

- *simple sugars*: carbohydrates that are readily and rapidly digested in the upper intestine
- *starches*: carbohydrates comprised of a small group of sugars connected together and rapidly digested in the upper intestine

- *complex carbohydrates*: carbohydrates that are connected together but cannot be digested and absorbed in the upper intestinal tract; they must be fermented by bacteria in the hindgut

The simple sugars and starches are also known as "non-structural carbohydrates." These are digested by enzymes and absorbed in the foregut, with some digestion and absorption happening in the stomach, and most occurring in the small intestine.

The complex "structural carbohydrates" are elements like *cellulose, pectin, fructan,* and *hemicellulose* that are digested with the help of microorganisms in the hindgut. In horses, a fermentation process converts these fiber components into volatile fatty acids (VFAs), which provide 30 to 70 percent of the horse's total digestible energy needs. Cellulose and hemicellulose are the non-seed, non-fruit parts of plants found in leaves, stems and hulls. Lignin (the fiber that gives plants their rigidity) is 100 percent indigestible by horses or microorganisms in the hindgut, and is instead pushed through the hindgut to become part of the manure. Lignin benefits the horse by helping maintain gut motility.

Both structural and non-structural carbohydrates are energy sources for horses. Structural carbohydrates are digested slowly, and provide sustained energy. Non-structural carbohydrates are digested rapidly and energy is released quickly for short bursts of activity. Understanding the difference between non-structural carbohydrates and structural carbohydrates, and how each type is calculated in the diet, can be an important guide to maintaining healthy weight and a more balanced metabolism in easy keepers and metabolic horses.

Calculating Non-structural Carbohydrates (NSC)

There are two methods of calculating NSC percentage. One method commonly used by feed companies and some veterinarians is to take the ethanol-soluble carbohydrates (ESC) analysis and add the starch analysis to get the NSC. The ESC is simple sugars only and does not include the fructans. Using this method, the NSC should be 10 or below for metabolic horses and easy keepers. Plant scientists, nutritionists and some veterinarians take the Water Soluble Carbohydrates (WSC) number, which includes the fructans and the ESC, then add the starch number to get a total NSC. For metabolic horses this needs to be 14 or below.

For example, I went looking for the NSC percentage of a particular feed labeled as safe for metabolic horses. The ESC was 4.0% and the starch was 11.0% for a total of 15% NSC. But this calculation was made without WSC — so at 15% for the sugars and starch combined, this feed is significantly higher than the 10% or below recommended for the ESC plus starch calculations.

Another low-starch feed comes in at 7% starch and 4% sugar (ESC) for a total of 11% NSC—just a tad over the 10-percent-or-less NSC recommended value.

A brand of alfalfa pellets use WSC plus starch to arrive at the NSC. For their alfalfa pellet it is: 7% WSC and 1% starch for a total of 8% NSC.

Average sugar (ESC) and starch content of common feed ingredients:

(values provided by Equi-Analytical Laboratories)

Ingredient	% Sugar (ESC)	% Starch	% Non-Structural Carbohydrates (NSC)
Rice Bran	6.2	17.7	21.2
Oats	4.8	44.4	54.1
Beet Pulp	10.7	1.4	12.3
Soybean Hulls	4.3	1.9	6.3
Soybean Meal	14.3	2.1	16.2
Wheat Bran	8.3	22.8	31.1
Wheat Middlings	10.1	26.2	32.0

A note on fructans and laminitis

Fructans are complex carbohydrates found in grasses, legumes, apples, garlic, rye, chicory, wheat, and barley. Oats do not contain fructans. Although it is still being researched, a link has been suggested between their consumption and development of the debilitating hoof disease laminitis. Currently there are two basic theories of fructans and their relationship to laminitis in horses: that fructans are a direct cause of pasture-associated laminitis in horses; and, contrarily, that pasture-associated laminitis is actually an endocrine disorder marked by an abnormal insulin response.

Researchers have categorized laminitis into three main types:

- Systemic (inflammatory/intestinal events where the horse is systemically ill)
- Weight bearing (contralateral limb laminitis, resulting from one foot compensating for another that is injured)
- Endocrine (metabolic/hormonal disturbances)

A 2011 study on insulin-induced laminitis found that laminitis occurring in insulin-resistant horses is accompanied by the intake of large amounts of non-structural carbohydrate-rich pasture. Since fructans are structural carbohydrates, this would support the theory that fructans do *not* cause pasture-associated laminitis. However, a fructan overload in the hindgut can cause changes in the hindgut microflora, which alters bacterial population balance and can cause a rapid rise of gram positive bacteria. This change in the hindgut bacteria may produce inflammation, a profound drop in pH and a rise in endotoxin levels. If laminitis resulted, this would be a systemic form of the disease.

Fats

Fats, also known as triglycerides, serve both structural and metabolic functions. They provide three times the energy of carbohydrates, and have a linear, chain-like molecular structure. In fact, they're categorized according to their length and the nutritional roles they play:

- *short-chain*: made by the horse in the hindgut (volatile fatty acids)
- *medium-chain*: found primarily in coconut oil and mother's milk; not stored, but used primarily for organ energy and muscle fuel; digested in the small intestine with bile from the liver
- *long-chain*: found in vegetable oils, fish, seeds, nuts; stored by the body during stress; digested in the small intestine with bile from the liver (note: Metabolic horses and easy keepers should avoid long-chain fats, as stress will increase cortisol production, resulting in the body storing more fat.)

Choosing the right fat sources for horses

There are many different fat sources for horses: oils, powders, fresh grass and nuts, along with specific seeds and plants. With so many different sources of fats, it's important to know the quality of the starting material—that is, how the source plant is cultivated and how it's processed. These factors have a profound impact on whether the dietary fat derived from a source will ultimately increase or decrease stress on the GI tract and the body system at large.

Some horses need fat for energy, while some horses need the calories from fat to maintain or gain weight. Horses with specific metabolic imbalances like polysaccharide storage myopathy (PSSM) or equine polysaccharide storage myopathy (EPSM) need fat because they can't metabolize carbohydrates. Some horses need additional omega-3 fatty acids from fat, and/or vitamin E. Horses with hindgut ulcers need a fat source that provides gamma-linolenic acid (GLA), an omega-6.

Fats for weight gain or weight maintenance (the hard keepers)

> My favorite fat source for these horses is rice bran powder, and I'm picky about it; I prefer organic, and I always check the arsenic levels (rices grown in California tend to have the lowest). Rice bran also provides fiber and protein, containing up to 15 percent of the latter. Being high in phosphorus, it needs to be balanced with a calcium source like timothy or alfalfa pellets/cubes, and also balanced with additional omega-3s because it is high in omega-6. Rice bran oil provides 100 percent fat, although I generally don't go to that route, as the oil is usually highly processed and extracted with toxic solvents; however, rice bran oil that is cold-pressed is a good choice.

Fats for energy

> My top picks in this category are coconut oil and coconut meal. The oil is a medium-chain fat, so it is readily used by the body for muscle and organ energy. Among potential fat sources for horses, it's a great choice for metabolic animals needing energy, because medium-chain fats are not stored in the body the way long-chain fats are (such as corn, soy, canola, vegetable or rice oils). Another benefit of coconut oil is lauric acid, which produces *2-mono-lauren*, an important component for immune support. What's more, coconut

oil has demonstrated the ability to maintain glycogen levels in muscle, which results in less fatigue with performance horses.

Fats high in omega-3s

Chia is my top choice for omega-3 supplementation from seeds. These seeds provide other benefits as well: they slow the digestion of carbohydrates (which is especially important for metabolic horses and easy keepers); they work like psyllium to remove sand from the GI tract; and they provide the amino acid proline, which is the major constituent of collagen. Flax is also, of course, a great source of omega-3s and my second choice for omega-3 supplementation from seeds.

If I want to feed a high omega-3 oil, my top pick is camelina oil. Also known as "false flax", camelina oil not only provides the ideal 2:1 ratio of omega-3:omega-6, but is one of the richest sources of vitamin E in the form of alpha, beta and gamma tocopherols. Camelina oil is also cold-pressed, meaning no solvent extraction during processing.

Fat sources for horses with metabolic imbalances

A high-fat diet is extremely important for horses with metabolic imbalances such as EPSM or PSSM. Some nutritionists recommend cups of corn oil per day. I prefer higher-quality oils that have not been processed into the nutritional wasteland described earlier. Higher-quality oils don't need to be fed in the same high amounts necessary when feeding lower-quality, solvent-extracted oils like corn, vegetable, rice, and soy. My choice for these animals is camelina oil or hemp seed oil combined with coconut meal (*Cool Stance*) or a combination of coconut meal and a GMO-free rice bran called *Renew Gold.*

Fat sources for hindgut ulcers

Hempseed oil is one of the few plant-sourced oils (along with borage seed oil and primrose oil) that provides the unique omega-6 gamma-linolenic acid (GLA). GLA plays an important role in the regulation of prostaglandins—lipid compounds that regulate inflammation, hormones, cell growth, and vascular constriction or dilation in smooth muscle cells. (Misoprostol, a drug commonly used to treat hindgut ulcers is a synthetic prostaglandin.) GLA helps regulate by increasing the anti-inflammatory prostaglandin PGE1. Hempseed oil is cold-pressed and free of solvents. Like coconut oil, hempseed oil has also demonstrated the ability to maintain glycogen levels in muscle, resulting in less fatigue for performance horses.

Fats for vitamin E supplementation

Once again, camelina oil stands out for its high inclusion of the vitamin E family of tocopherols. Almonds (sliced or ground), sunflower seeds and wheat germ (cold-pressed!) are also good choices. I often rotate these vitamin E sources to give horses some variety.

Fat sources to avoid

These are the fat sources for horses that I steer clear of, and the reasons why:

- *corn oil*: genetically modified; processed with high heat that causes oxidative damage to the essential fatty acids and denatures nutrient content; extracted with the neurotoxin hexane; deodorized and bleached after processing to reduce the rancid odor.
- *canola oil*: for all of the above reasons.
- *soy oil*: same as corn and canola, plus the fact that soy is higher in phytoestrogens than almost any other food source. These soy phytoestrogens can disrupt healthy endocrine function.
- *vegetable oil*: a blend of the above corn and soy oil preparations.
- *rice bran oil*: Rice from Arkansas, Texas, Louisiana, Mississippi, and Missouri contains high levels of arsenic, which makes the oil from rice grown in these states undesirable. However, rice bran oil from cold pressed, California-grown rice is a good choice.
- *wheat germ oil*: except for the cold-pressed, organic version. If the label says "vitamin E fortified" or "added", it's a clear indication of processing with high heat and denaturing of the oil by solvent extraction with hexane. The vitamin E is added after processing since the processing destroys the vitamin E present in the wheat germ itself.

Equine fat source alternatives to oil

A good alternative to coconut oil is coconut meal, which provides 10 percent fat as well as 20 percent fiber, 20 percent protein, and an NSC value of 10. Coconut meal is high in phosphorus, so adding more calcium (via beet pulp or alfalfa pellets/cubes) will balance the phosphorus. According to HorseFeedAnalysis.org, coconut meal provides 0.6 percent phosphorus and 0.08 percent calcium.

Along with coconut meal, whole rice bran is another fat-source alternative to oils. With its high omega-6 content, it is important to add flax or chia to increase the omega-3 content. Rice is also high in phosphorus and needs to be balanced with added calcium. Organic whole rice bran is preferred, of course, but be aware that a percentage of rice grown in the U.S. is GMO. Always check with your supplier about the arsenic content of rice bran.

Quality matters

It's true that products like cold-pressed oils, rice bran from California, sun-dried or kiln-dried coconut meal can be more expensive. However, higher quality food means less stress to the GI tract; in many cases higher quality means greater **bioavailability** (see the chart, next page), which translates into reduced amounts needed per feeding. In addition, the horses get the benefits of all nutrients and co-factors inherent to each of the oils and other healthy-fat foods.

Percent of Absorption/Bioavailability of Minerals and Nutrients

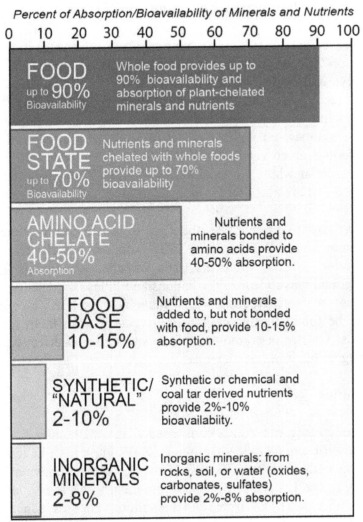

| 0 | 10 | 20 | 30 | 40 | 50 | 60 | 70 | 80 | 90 | 100 |

FOOD up to **90%** Bioavailability — Whole food provides up to 90% bioavailability and absorption of plant-chelated minerals and nutrients

FOOD STATE up to **70%** Bioavailability — Nutrients and minerals chelated with whole foods provide up to 70% bioavailability

AMINO ACID CHELATE 40-50% Absorption — Nutrients and minerals bonded to amino acids provide 40-50% absorption.

FOOD BASE 10-15% — Nutrients and minerals added to, but not bonded with food, provide 10-15% absorption.

SYNTHETIC/ "NATURAL" 2-10% — Synthetic or chemical and coal tar derived nutrients provide 2%-10% bioavailabiity.

INORGANIC MINERALS 2-8% — Inorganic minerals: from rocks, soil, or water (oxides, carbonates, sulfates) provide 2%-8% absorption.

Resources
Vinson, J.A., Nutrient availability, chemical and biological aspects. Royal Society of Chemistry. 1989
Southgate, D.A.T., Johnson, I.T., Fenwick, G.R.: Nutrient availability: chemical and biological aspects;
AFRC Institute of Food Research, Norwich.

Vitamins, Minerals, Enzymes, and Other Nutrients

Reference books tell us that "nutrients" are substances in food that provide nourishment essential for living organisms to survive and grow. Strange thing is, many of the nutrients in feeds and supplements are *not* from food, but are the processing byproducts of the petroleum and coal tar industry. These synthesized replicas of vitamins may look identical to the food-sourced versions under the microscope, but they lack the essential whole composition of important cofactors found in food that are essential for bioavailability.

Albert Szent-Györgyi was the first to isolate ascorbic acid (vitamin C) in 1931, and in 1937 won the Nobel Prize in Medicine for his discovery. His impetus for finding the compound was to learn why lemons and limes cured scurvy, a disease that afflicted sailors. Although he isolated ascorbic acid, he found that he couldn't cure scurvy with it. In other words, isolated ascorbic acid was not nearly as effective as eating whole limes and lemons.

Vitamins

These are organic compounds needed in small quantities to sustain life and include vitamins A, D, B complex, C, E, and K. Horses make their own Vitamin C and B complex, but vitamins A, D, E, and K must be obtained from dietary sources or, in the case of vitamin D, from direct sunlight. Forages generally supply vitamins A, E, and K. However, hay that is harvested late, improperly stored, or grown in poor soils can have low vitamin content, particularly A and E. Supplementation is necessary, especially if the horse is not on fresh pasture.

Minerals

Nutrient minerals are essential elements that cannot be manufactured by the body and are necessary for various biological processes and functions. Minerals are divided into two groups: macrominerals and microminerals (or trace minerals). Calcium, phosphorus, magnesium, sodium, potassium, chloride, and sulfur are considered macrominerals. Trace minerals include boron, chromium, copper, zinc, iron, manganese, and selenium.

Minerals are essential for enzyme reactions; they work as co-factors for enzymes. They help maintain the pH balance within the body, facilitate transport of nutrients across cell membranes, maintain nerve conduction, help contract and relax muscles, regulate tissue growth, and provide structural and functional support for the body. The microminerals in particular are important for digestion, growth, and hormone regulation. They assist in the transport of oxygen to cells, support maintenance and repair of tissue and bone, and play critical roles in the synthesis of DNA, proteins, and enzymes.

Minerals in feeds and supplements

Most minerals used in feeds and supplements are in their inorganic form—that is, ground-up rock. We see these forms commonly as oxides, carbonates, and sulfates. In order to utilize these inorganic substances, the body must find something organic to attach to the mineral in order to pull it through the intestinal wall. This process of attachment is called chelation. The most common chelators used by the body are free amino acids.

Plants get their minerals from soil organisms that deliver the nutrients via a superhighway made by worms. Soil that is nurtured and not compacted will have more worms and better super highways for the bacteria and fungi to deliver nutrients. Plants do their own chelation of minerals, binding them with free amino acids. When horses eat plants their bodies get minerals in their most bioavailable form. The challenge is that a lot of the soils in the U.S. are mineral deficient, particularly of the trace minerals. *It is therefore essential when feeding a whole food diet to your horse that you supplement with a multivitamin/mineral.*

Enzymes

These are biological catalysts, responsible for facilitating and regulating all aspects of cell metabolism. Some enzymes are important for digestion, helping to break down proteins, carbohydrates, fiber, and fats. There are three basic types of these enzymes:

- **Metabolic enzymes** speed up the chemical reactions within cells for energy production. Every organ, tissue, and cell depends upon the action of metabolic enzymes.

- **Digestive enzymes** break food down into nutrients and waste.

- **Food enzymes** are naturally contained in whole food, and help break down that particular food. Whole food that has not been cooked provides these food enzymes, which reduces the body's requirement to produce more digestive enzymes. Those that are not used in digestion can then be used for other important processes. Food enzymes are very sensitive to heat and break down at temperatures exceeding 116 degrees. Commercial feeds typically do not contain food enzymes, as they are destroyed in processing.

Basic Nutritional Information on Whole Food Components

Fiber and protein foods

alfalfa (pellets or cubes): 15-18% protein, 30% fiber

timothy (pellets or cubes): 9-10% protein, 35% fiber

alfalfa/timothy (pellets or cubes): 12% protein, 32% fiber

beet pulp (Speedi-Beet): 10% protein, 16% fiber

beet pulp shreds without molasses: 8% protein, 18% fiber

Quick-burn energy foods

whole oats: 11-12% protein, 53% starch, 12% fiber

rolled barley: 12-14% protein, 64% starch, 6% fiber

Long-burn energy foods

rice bran: 10-12% protein, 18-22% fat, 13% fiber

coconut meal (Cool Stance): 20% protein, 8% fat, 22% fiber

Renew Gold: 15% protein, 15% fat, 22% fiber

hemp oil: 99.7% fat, 3% vitamin E

camelina oil: 99.5% fat, 5% vitamin E

coconut oil: (per 1 ounce): 13.6 grams fat

Essential fatty acids

flax seeds: (per 2 ounces): 24% protein, 40% fat, 25% fiber

chia seeds: (per 2 ounces): 18% protein, 30% fat, 26% fiber

High-NSC foods not recommended for easy keepers and metabolic horses

barley: 61.7% NSC

oats: 54.1% NSC

rice bran: 21.2% NSC

soybean meal: 16.2% NSC

wheat middlings: 32% NSC

wheat bran: 30.8% NSC

Gut Microbiota and Equine Health

The microbiota (or microbiome) is the diverse community of microorganisms that live within the bodies, and particularly the digestive tracts, of nearly all animals. There is a tremendous amount of research going on in the US, the EU, and Asia focused on the importance of the microbiota to body system health. As this research has illuminated, mammals including horses, dogs, and humans actually contain more microbial genome than mammalian-species genome. In humans alone, up to 100 trillion bacteria representing 500 to 1000 different species coexist in the GI tract.

The intestinal microbiota play crucial roles in metabolic, nutritional, physiological, and immunological processes. The metabolic activities lead to the production of short-chain fatty acids, certain vitamins (K, B12, folic acid) and amino acids. The intestinal microbiota also participate in the defense against pathogens, the development/maturation/maintenance of the GI sensory and motoric functions, as well as maintenance of a healthy intestinal barrier and mucosal immune system.

Environment, food, and DNA play an important part in determining the unique microbiota of our bodies. Each horse, each dog and each human has a unique colony of microbiota at work. There is overlap, by the way; people who live with dogs, for instance, will share some of the same micro-organisms as their canines.

Other environmental factors abound. Babies that are born through the birth canal share many of the same microorganisms as their mother, while a child born by Caesarean section does not get the microorganisms that reside in the birth canal. Farm workers have different proportions of bacterial colonies in their systems than city workers. If you garden without gloves, you expose your skin to a host of beneficial microorganisms from the soil. Similarly, when horses and dogs roll in the grass or dirt, they're helping colonize their largest organ—the skin.

Microbiota of the GI tract: balance is key

The type and number of microbial species that colonize the GI tract depend on several factors: the inflammatory state of the host, the presence of antibiotics or other medications, stress levels, diet, genetics, age, and a host of additional environmental factors. In any healthy body system, there are colonies of beneficial microorganisms, and colonies of potentially harmful microorganisms. The beneficial microbes help to keep the harmful ones in check. When this balance is disrupted, the harmful strains can take over. It's important to note that having a healthy body system does not mean eliminating *all* the harmful bacteria; it simply means that colonies of beneficial bacteria are larger and stronger than colonies of the harmful ones.

Viable probiotics: Live performers for GI health

Probiotics are what we call a variety of especially beneficial microbes that make up just a part of this vast microbiota. Viable or "live" probiotics are measured in "colony forming units" or CFUs. Viable probiotics are capable of adhesion to host mucosa in the GI tract; in fact, their ability to do this is a key determinant of probiotic efficacy. The higher the CFU rating of a probiotic dose, the greater the number of viable, beneficial bacteria that are present, capable of adhering and increasing colonization.

Since the microbiotic cell population of horses is estimated in the trillions, the probiotic number needed by horses is, at minimum, about 100 billion CFUs. For sick horses, the number of required CFUs can easily rise to 400 billion or more. The requirement for dogs is proportionally smaller, ranging from one to five billion CFUs.

> *Whether you're comparing probiotics for dogs or for horses, remember: If you cannot find a CFU number stated on the product label, it is not a viable probiotic.*

Remember too, that all of these microorganisms have their own dietary needs, which we call "prebiotics". Not to be confused with probiotics, prebiotics are simply food for the microbiota of the GI tract. They include fructo-oligosaccharides (FOS) like inulin (not "insulin") and other oligosaccharides. Common prebiotic foods for horses—and for their gut microbiota—include hay, grass, chicory root, dandelion greens, and bananas. Prebiotic sources for canines include beans, lentils, peas, fruits, and vegetables.

Yeast and Lactobacillus

Yeast probiotics (*Saccharomyces* and *Enterococcus* species) help ferment and break down fiber in the hindgut. *Lactobacillus* (lactic acid bacteria) are found throughout the GI tract, in the respiratory tract, and in the oral cavities. In Ayurvedic medicine (see Appendix A), yeasts can be either warming or heating to the GI tract, while milk (a source of *Lactobacillus* strains) is cooling. Horses or dogs with diarrhea will benefit from a cooling probiotic rather than a heating one. Horses that need to gain weight, and are not ulcer-prone, benefit from yeast probiotics. Older horses who have lost some of their "digestive fire" with age, also benefit from yeast probiotics. Ulcer horses or ulcer-sensitive horses benefit from the *Lactobacillus* probiotics (often indicated simply as "L." probiotics).

Bacteroidetes

Bacteroidetes are very interesting bacteria. Members of this phylum have colonized virtually all habitats on Earth, including soil, freshwater, oceans, and the GI tracts of mammals. Bacteroidetes are specialists in the degradation of high-molecular-weight organic matter: proteins and carbohydrates. Bacteroidetes' other contributions to the mammalian GI tract include interactions with the immune system for the activation of T-cell-mediated responses, and the limitation of GI tract colonization by potentially pathogenic bacteria. Resident gut Bacteroidetes produce butyrate, a volatile fatty acid that is an end product of colonic fermentation of carbohydrates. In the horse, this encompasses plant carbohydrates including fiber. Butyrate, like other volatile fatty acids, can be used as an energy source by horses.

A study published in 2012 set about characterizing the fecal microbiome of healthy horses compared to the fecal microbiome of horses with undifferentiated colitis. The bacteria that predominated in the healthy horses were: Firmicutes (68%), which includes lactobacilli and bifidobacteria, followed by Bacteriodetes (14%) and Proteobacteria (10%). In contrast, Bacteriodetes was the most abundant phylum (40%) among horses with colitis, followed by Firmicutes (30%) and Proteobacteria (18%). The study highlights the differences in the microbiome of healthy horses and horses with colitis.

In terms of keeping the good bacteria alive and healthy, remember: it's not only what the horses and dogs (and humans) eat that affects the microbiome; it's also how the food is grown and processed that affects the populations of beneficial bacteria in the GI tract. The simple fact that Bacteroidetes live in soil and water furthers our understanding of how chemical fertilizers and herbicides can affect the population of these beneficial bacteria. Minimally processed foods will have a higher concentration of microbiota than overly processed or heat-treated foods. Also, byproducts of whole foods—soy hulls for instance—will not contain the microbiota of the whole soybean itself.

According to one 2011 study, there is a strong connection between how a food is grown and processed and how the population of Bacteroidetes is affected:

> "This food connection points toward the fact that recurrent contacts between environmental and gut microbes can have beneficial effects. At the same time, it underlines the potential problem of our modern lifestyle and the consumption of hyper-hygenic, extensively processed food, depriving us of the environmental reservoirs of microbial genes that allow adaptation by lateral transfer." (Thomas F, Hehemann JH, et al. Environmental and Gut Bacteroidetes: The Food Connection. Front Microbiol. 2011; 2-93)

When to use viable probiotics

Viable probiotics for horses are recommended during periods of stress: shipping, hard training, competition, after worming, during and after antibiotic therapy, for idiopathic diarrhea (diarrhea of unknown origin), or during a change in diet. Horses that live out, have access to pasture and forage 24/7 do not need probiotics in most cases. Horses that are confined, however, with a limited amount of turnout, will benefit from a daily viable probiotic.

Canines that live on farms where they get to roll in dirt/grass may not need probiotics for dogs like suburban or city dogs will. However, exposure to chemical fertilizers, home cleaning products, pesticides, and herbicides do increase the need for daily viable probiotics.

Other considerations when giving probiotics

On the human side of antibiotic therapy, there are warnings against taking tetracycline with calcium/milk products. According to the FDA, this is not true for doxycycline, which is not markedly influenced by the simultaneous ingestion of food or milk. Accordingly, the *Merck Veterinary Manual* cautions that tetracycline absorption is decreased by milk and milk products, antacids, and iron preparations. However, these negative interactions are not as evident with the use of doxycycline and minocycline. In general, when using viable probiotics alongside antibiotics, it is a good idea to separate the two and not feed both simultaneously. Wait two to four hours after antibiotic administration before feeding a probiotic. In the post-antibiotic therapy phase, it is wise to continue with viable probiotics for as many days or weeks as the horse or dog was given antibiotics. This is to help support new, beneficial colonization of the GI tract.

If you are concerned about GMOs (genetically modified organisms), you will need to verify that the probiotics in your feed and supplements are GMO-free. Sugar is often used in the fermentation process of *Lactobacillus*, and the most common source for this in the US is beet pulp, which is predominately GMO. The yeast *Saccharomyces* includes over 1,000 subset strains, some of which are genetically modified. This includes not only probiotic yeast, but brewer's yeast and nutritional yeast.

Lastly, some probiotic-related points to remember when managing weight and healthy blood sugar in your horses:

- We love giving treats to our horses, but high sugar combined with high-starch foods may activate the Firmicutes biota and lower the Bacteroidetes numbers. Better to give a couple of carrot slices or apple slices.
- Low-starch horse feeds may indeed have low starch, yet they are often made with food byproducts, which could play a role in the population balance of the microbiota.
- Glyphosate is often used on hay fields to control weeds. Although the exact role this chemical plays in affecting the microbiome has yet to be determined, European studies have shown that glyphosate does affect the GI tracts of livestock and puts stress on the immune system.
- With our new understanding of the GI-tract benefits of spirulina, this needs to be an important component in the overall management of metabolic imbalances and the easy keepers.

- Let your horse get dirty! Microbes are transferred via the skin, and your horse will get some beneficial Bacteroidetes when he or she can roll in the grass or mud.

Microbiota and probiotics can be a somewhat complicated facet of equine nutrition, but the take-home messages are fairly straightforward: Each horse and dog has a unique microbiota that is best supported with a multi-strain probiotic. Remember to always check those CFUs on the label to make sure that you're using a viable probiotic. As detailed above, probiotics for horses need to show a CFU number in the hundred billions, not millions, for effective colonization of the GI tract, while probiotics for dogs need a CFU count in the low billions for the same efficacy. Proper support of the microbiota will pay off, helping take better GI care of your horses, dogs, and you.

Yeast

Yeasts are fascinating single-celled microorganisms that don't require sunlight or oxygen in order to live and grow, but instead get their energy from organic compounds in the environment. About 1,500 species are currently identified. They occur naturally on the skins of fruits and berries, on exudates secreted by cacti and other plants, in the soil, on insects, on our own skin, and even in deep ocean environments where a variety of species thrive. Yeast exist nearly everywhere in the wild, and yet they may also be one of the earliest domesticated organisms; archeologists working in Egypt have found baking chambers for yeast-raised bread that date back thousands of years.

Under anaerobic conditions (without oxygen), yeast converts sugar and starches into alcohol and carbon dioxide. This process is known as **fermentation**. Without yeast fermentation there would be no bread, wine, beer, root beer, kombucha, or kefir. Without yeast fermentation there would be no industrial ethanol production, nor would we have a wide variety of chemicals that are now produced with genetically engineered yeast, including phenolics, alkaloids, and specific amino acids such as lysine. Some biopharmaceuticals are produced from yeast, including insulin, vaccines for hepatitis, and human serum albumin.

Yeast for horses

The two most common strains of yeast used in equine feeds and supplements are *Saccharomyces cerevisiae* and *Saccharomyces boulardii*. These yeasts function in the hindgut of horses helping to digest dry matter and organic matter. The yeasts are commonly fed in one of two forms: "yeast culture," or "live/active" yeast.

Yeast culture, also known as yeast fermentation product, has been processed so that it is heat stable and can withstand high temperatures. Yeast culture cannot colonize the hindgut because it is not *viable* or alive. Yeast culture cannot reproduce because the yeast has been inactivated. Yeast culture is the most predominant form of yeast in feeds and some supplements.

Active yeast, also known as viable or live yeast, is capable of colonization. Several European studies highlight the increased digestibility of fiber in the hindgut with live yeast. Active yeast is measured in CFUs (colony forming units) just like other active probiotics such as yogurt.

Yeast and the hindgut

Changes to the pH of the hindgut can occur when soluble carbohydrates from grains or grasses overload the small intestine and pass to the large intestine where microbial fermentation occurs. Rapid fermentation occurs with accumulation of lactic acid bacteria, which changes the pH of the hindgut, causing suppression of the fiber-digesting bacteria. Changes to the pH of the hindgut can cause colic, laminitis, and increased gas accumulation as the abundant lactate-producing bacteria take over. Studies in the UK have shown that lactic acid levels were lower and cecal pH higher in horses fed a high starch diet supplemented with live yeast.

- **Brewers yeast** is a byproduct of beer-making and like baking bread, uses *S. cerevisiae* yeast. It is inactivated by heat then made into powder or flakes known as brewer's yeast. Brewer's yeast is an excellent source of B-vitamins, GTF (glucose tolerance factor) chromium, magnesium, protein, nucleic acid, and all the essential amino acids. Brewer's yeast, due to its inactivation, does not function as a probiotic.

- **Nutritional yeast** is made with *S. cerevisiae* yeast and grown on a medium like molasses, or grains, or sugar beets. It is a deactivated yeast. Nutritional yeast is made specifically for supplementation, and does provide the same nutritional components as brewer's yeast, but is less bitter and more palatable. It does not function as a probiotic.

- **Selenium yeast** is produced by fermenting *S. cerevisiae* in a selenium-rich media. The organic form of selenium provided by selenium yeast has been shown to provide a higher bioavailability of selenium. Selenium yeast has been associated with increased ability to counteract oxidative stress with its antioxidant properties, and helps with immune response, growth, and reproduction.

- **Live, Viable Yeast:** this is *S. cerevisiae or S. boulardii* in a form capable of being actively probiotic and able to colonize the GI tract, particularly the hindgut. *S. boulardii* does have some action on the small intestine as well.

When to supplement with yeast

Live yeast improves fiber fermentative capacity and other aspects of digestion. It helps to ameliorate potentially detrimental changes to the hindgut population and environment, particularly when feeds are high in starch. It also helps reduce overpopulation of lactic acid bacteria in the hindgut and increase the level of activity of cellulolytic bacteria (the bacteria that break down cellulose). Live yeast can be a supportive food for horses with hindgut ulcers and colitis, and can be beneficial for hard-keepers during or after antibiotic therapy, and during times of high stress such as shipping and competing.

How to Feed a Whole Food Diet

One of the most common questions I am asked is, how much do I feed? The answer: it depends on the energy needs of your horse. A high-performance horse generally burns more calories than a horse in light work. An easy keeper doesn't need more starch and sugar calories from oats or barley or even rice bran. The literature we have available on how horses were fed in the 19th century highlights how hard those horses worked, and how many energy calories they needed. Grains such as oats and corn provided the calories. Many horses today don't need those grain calories, or don't need them in very high amounts.

Always remember:

The number one food for horses, no matter what their level of work, is hay, pasture, forage. The whole food diet is focused on that elemental aspect of the equine digestive tract, which is why the base of whole food feed is timothy or alfalfa pellets or cubes, and/or beet pulp.

And...

always have available a salt block or free-choice loose mineral salt.

High-performance horses

These are horses working and competing at the top levels of their sport. Their energy requirements may depend on higher starch foods like oats, and a fat source for maintaining weight such as rice bran. An easy keeper who is a high-performance horse may do better with a medium-chain fat such as coconut meal as a fat/energy source because the body will use a medium-chain fat for muscle energy. The NSC of coconut meal is 11, making it ideal for the high-performance easy keeper.

Sample diet for high-performance (not an easy keeper):

Per meal, fed three or four times per day:
- 1 quart alfalfa pellets
- 2-4 cups Renew Gold (blend of rice bran and coconut meal) or straight rice bran
- 1-2 cups whole oats
- ¼ cup flax seeds or chia seeds
- multi vitamin/mineral

Sample diet for high-performance easy keeper:

Per meal, fed three times per day:
- 1 quart alfalfa pellets
- 1-2 cups Cool Stance (coconut meal)
- ¼ cup chia seeds
- multi vitamin/mineral

Performance horses

These are horses training five to six days per week, and that have not yet reached the elite, high-performance level of competition.

Sample diet for performance (not an easy keeper):

Per meal, fed two or three times per day:
- 3-4 cups alfalfa pellets or timothy pellets
- ½ - 1 cup Renew Gold (blend of rice bran and coconut meal) or straight rice bran

- ½ – 1 cup whole oats (if needed for calories or energy)
- ¼ cup flax seeds or chia seeds
- multi vitamin/mineral

Sample diet for performance easy keeper:

Per meal, fed two or three times per day:
- 2-3 cups alfalfa or timothy pellets
- ½ cup coconut meal
- ¼ cup chia seeds
- multi vitamin/mineral

Horses in light work

These are the pleasure horses, ridden lightly two to four times per week.

Sample diet for light-work (not an easy keeper):

Per meal, fed two times per day:
- 1-2 cups alfalfa or timothy pellets
- ¼ - ½ cup Renew Gold (blend of rice bran and coconut meal)
- ¼ cup flax seed or chia seeds
- multi vitamin/mineral

Sample diet for light-work easy keeper:

Per meal, fed two times per day
- 1-2 cups alfalfa or timothy pellets
- ¼ cup chia seeds
- multi vitamin/mineral

Note that these are examples of the typical food components in the whole food diet based on the horse's caloric and energy needs. The amounts of each ingredient will vary from horse to horse.

Hard Keepers

I have found that thoroughbreds can be harder keepers than many warmbloods or quarterhorses. Their metabolism makes oats one of the great foods for them. If your horse is a hard keeper with thoroughbred blood, you will find that oats with alfalfa pellets and a fat source like rice bran is a super combination for a healthy weight. Active yeast probiotics with a high CFU (colony-forming units) count help digest fiber in the hindgut and can help many horses put on weight.

Metabolic Horses

Diet is one of the keys to managing metabolic diseases in horses. Avoid grains, soy, and rice bran. Make sure you know the NSC of your hay. Don't let a metabolic horse fast for longer than three hours. Slow feeders for hay can be very helpful for metabolic horses by providing hay over a longer period thus reducing fasting time. Particularly with insulin resistance, you want to keep them moving, exercising, and burning calories.

Senior Horses

As horses age, they can start to loose topline in their mid to late teens and on into their twenties. Maintaining or building topline in older horses can be challenging. Alfalfa is beneficial as well as additional protein sources like un-denatured whey protein, hemp protein and egg protein.

Check selenium and vitamin E levels in your horse to make sure these two important nutrients are not deficient, which can affect muscle maintenance.

I feed active yeast probiotics in winter to my senior horses to help with circulation and digestion of fiber in the hindgut. This helps them utilize the fiber foods I am feeding them. The warming action of active yeast probiotics can also help them stay warm.

Salt

Most horses need additional salt in their diet. If they are on electrolytes, they may need only one additional teaspoon of Celtic sea salt or Himalayan salt. Horses not on electrolytes will benefit from one tablespoon of Celtic sea salt or Himalayan salt per day. These salts are more beneficial than table salt, as they contain 70 trace minerals plus electrolytes and magnesium. These salts are commonly sun-dried, which is the extent of their processing. Table salt is so highly refined that all the supportive trace minerals are taken out, including the important macro-mineral magnesium. Table salt is also bleached to give it the pure white color.

Supplements

Supplements should augment and support the diet, not detract from it. Ingredients in supplements are as important to scrutinize as ingredients in processed feeds. Read the list of inactive ingredients as carefully as the active ingredients, and remember that supplements and feed ingredients are listed by weight, not volume.

When you are looking to add a supplement to your horse's program, read each ingredient and ask yourself, *is this going to increase stress on the GI tract, or decrease stress on the GI tract?*

I have my own personal list of supplement ingredients that I won't feed my horses: artificial and natural flavorings, sucrose, dextrose, maltodextrin, preservatives, coal tar and petroleum-derived vitamins, MSM, dried distillers grains, wheat byproducts, soy byproducts, vegetable oil, corn oil, soy oil, mineral oil, amino acids made through biotechnology, and genetically modified yeasts.

It is up to each owner, rider, and trainer to come up with his or her own personal list of ingredients that you won't feed. Once you have your *don'ts*, it's a lot easier to read labels and not get sucked into marketing claims.

A word about water

Horses can go longer without food than they can without water. Maintaining hydration is of the utmost importance 365 days a year. Water contamination from agricultural runoff, well water exposure to pesticides, herbicides and heavy metals, and city water with high amounts of chlorine and chlorine byproducts can all affect a horse's water consumption.

If your horse is not drinking enough, you may want to consider a filtering system or a convenient hose-attachment filter to improve your horse's hydration.

Feeding for Immune Health

The immune system's job is to protect and eliminate external pathogens such as bacteria, viruses, parasites, and allergens, as well as internal pathogens like cancer cells, toxins, metabolic waste, and damaged tissues. The old horseman's adage, "The health of the horse begins in the gut" is important to remember, because the GI tract plays a key role in the immune system. A digestive tract that is unhealthy can lead to an overloaded immune system that can lose the ability to respond to pathogens. A fatigued immune system can make the horse more prone to infections. On the other hand, an immune system that over-responds or is in hyper-drive creates more inflammation. A good example of this is allergies or hives, which are a clear indication that the immune system is overreacting.

Healthy functionality of the equine immune system can be negatively affected by a few common factors:

- *Stress* can come from environmental factors or chronic conditions such as ulcers, as well as from the pressures of competitions, shipping, injuries, lay-up, metabolic imbalances, and daily training.
- *Nutritional deficiencies* can result from insufficient and/or low-quality forage and hay. Deficiencies can also occur when feeding processed feeds if the recommended amount per day is not fed. Some nutritional deficiencies are a result of metabolic issues such as PSSM, EPSM, and HYPP.
- *Age* is a factor because older horses tend to have weaker immune systems due to the aging process.

But no matter what causes the immune system to be weakened, the result is the same: pathogens being more easily able to breach the defense systems of the body. It is often said that the GI tract is the seat of the immune system. This is because 60 percent of lymphatic tissue surrounds the digestive tract, providing barriers to infection and playing a critical role in immune responses. What we feed is not only about protein, fat, fiber, carbohydrates, and calories; it is also about the quality of the food itself. The question we want to ask of every feed and supplement we use is: *Are the ingredients going to decrease stress on the GI tract or increase stress on the GI tract?* Fortunately, there are specific foods that can aid and support a healthy immune system.

Bovine Colostrum

Bovine colostrum may well be one of the most important whole foods on the planet. Widely used by human athletes around the world—and designated as a whole food by the International Olympic Committee—bovine colostrum is an important food for equine athletes as well. It is capable of speeding up the healing process and reducing stress-induced inflammation. With over 70 growth factors and over 80 immune factors, this whole food is a powerhouse of cellular, tissue, GI tract, and immune support. A high-quality colostrum derived from grass-fed, antibiotic-free cows will provide proline-rich polypeptides (PRPs) that have a unique ability to regulate the thymus gland (the master gland of the immune system), as well as immunoglobulins (antibodies) that are critical to a healthy immune response.

Immunoglobulin A (IgA) is especially important in mucosal immunity; it is an essential protective factor against infectious agents, allergens, and foreign proteins that enter the body via the mouth, nose, upper respiratory tracts, and intestines. (Takahasi I, Kiyono H. 1999) Immunoglobulin G (IgG) is an essential antibody because it is effective against multiple pathogens, many of which are now becoming resistant to antibiotics. One of the richest sources of this immunoglobulin is bovine colostrum. In fact, bovine colostrum's activity is measured by the percentage of IgG it contains. The higher the IgG content, the more potent the colostrum.

To help control overreaction of the immune system, bovine colostrum also contains lactoferrin, a premier immune regulator. Lactoferrin can regulate the production of inflammatory cytokines, which the body overproduces in many auto-immune conditions such as allergies and inflammatory bowel disease.

Some of immune conditions and situations with which bovine colostrum can help include:

- equine protozoal myeloencephalitis (EPM)
- Lyme disease
- uveitis
- allergies
- inflammatory bowel
- chronic inflammation
- wound healing
- acute infections
- when the horse travels
- during periods of stress

Spirulina

Known as blue-green algae, Spirulina is a phytonutrient-dense food. Recent studies have shown that it can augment interferon production and can protect against intracellular pathogens. In animal studies, spirulina has shown to be an effective immunomodulatory, suppressing the release of histamines and therefore making spirulina a very important food for horses with allergies.

Medicinal mushrooms

Used for thousands of years in traditional Chinese medicine (TCM), recent research demonstrates the remarkable immunological properties of these fungi. The most studied medicinal mushrooms include Turkey Tail, Reishi, Shiitake, Cordycepts and Maitake.

Coconut oil

Coconut oil provides two important immune support compounds: *lauric acid and caprylic acid.* Lauric acid is converted into monolaurin in the body, which has anti-viral, anti-bacterial, and anti-protozoa properties. Caprylic acid is beneficial for dealing with fungal infections.

Antioxidant fruits

These include apples, oranges, pomegranates, kiwi, papaya, mangoes, and blueberries that provide specific nutrients and antioxidant compounds such as vitamin C, quercitin, bioflavonoids, polyphenols, and anthocyanins. Antioxidants can help reduce oxidative stress and reduce inflammation.

Antioxidant vegetables

Carrots, squash, pumpkin seeds, kale, and alfalfa provide important antioxidant vitamins such as beta-carotene, vitamin C and vitamin E.

Adaptogenic herbs

Plants categorized as *adaptogens* must specifically be found to reduce stress, be completely safe and non-toxic, and have a normalizing action (neither overstimulating nor inhibiting normal body system functions). Adaptogens exert a tonifying effect. Key adaptogenic herbs for horses include ashwaganda, holy basil, ginseng, maca, rhodiola rosea, and schisandra.

Flax and chia seeds

These mucilaginous seeds coat the mucous membranes and prevent irritation of the nerve endings. This is especially beneficial to the GI tract. Flax and chia seeds are excellent food sources of omega-3 fatty acids and provide anti-inflammatory action.

Hemp seed oil

Hemp seed oil is an excellent source of gamma linoleic acid (GLA), which the body uses to reduce levels of inflammatory prostaglandins. GLA is particularly beneficial to the GI tract and specific to the hindgut.

Camelina oil

This oil provides the perfect ratio of omega 3:6:9, and is one of the richest available food sources of the antioxidant vitamin E.

Turmeric and boswellia

Inflammation can be the result of an overstimulated immune system, causing pain both acute and chronic. Chronic inflammation (inflammation that is uncontrolled) can lead to diseases including cancer, degenerative joint disease, digestive tract disorders (intestinal bloating, frequent bouts of diarrhea, gas, constipation), asthma, inflammatory bowel disease and ulcerative colitis.

When it comes to fighting inflammation, turmeric and boswellia are the Batman and Robin of traditional Chinese and Ayurvedic medicine. Known as *jiang huang* in TCM and *kanchani* ("Golden Goddess") in Ayurvedic medicine, turmeric is a spice and a member of the ginger family. It contains hundreds of molecular constituents with a variety of biological actions. One of these constituents is *curcumin*, which demonstrates strong COX-2 inhibition—that is, it blocks a molecule called cyclooxgenase-2, an enzyme that promotes pain, swelling and inflammation in the body. Boswellia is a tree that grows primarily in India, Northern Africa, and the Middle East. Commonly known as Indian frankincense, the resin of Boswellia has been used internally and externally for thousands of years, particularly by the Hindus, Babylonians, Persians, Romans, Chinese, and Egyptians in religious, cultural, and embalming ceremonies. Boswellia's active constituents are the boswellic acids, particularly acetyl-11-keto-beta-boswellic acid (AKBA). AKBA inhibits the inflammatory enzyme 5-lipoxygenase (5-LOX), which stimulates other pro-inflammatory molecules called leukotrienes which, in turn, have been linked to arthritis, asthma, and inflammatory bowel diseases.

Remember, the foundation of a healthy immune system begins in the gut. Reducing stress, and providing quality hay and forage and feed is essential. If your horse shows early signs of stress it is important not to ignore those signs.

Feeding for Joint Health

Several years ago, a friend of mine had a total knee replacement. He had osteoarthritis from the bangs and blows of playing college football—not an activity known for supporting joint health. When I asked him how the recovery was going, his answer surprised me: "The hardest part of recovering from this surgery has been my diet," he said. His surgeon and his sports medicine doctor had rather strongly recommended he change his eating habits by including more fruits and vegetables, less red meat, eliminating processed sugars, staying away from processed foods, drinking more water, adding more omega-3s to his diet, and losing at least 30 pounds through managed diet and exercise.

The reasons for all of these specific dietary recommendations in the wake of a knee replacement will become apparent in the next several pages. Feeding and supplementing for maximum joint health can be best accomplished by first understanding a few things about the body systems and substances involved.

The food-joint connection

The expression "garbage in, garbage out" can be applied to the GI tract. After all, in traditional Chinese and Ayurvedic medicine, the focus of health begins with the GI tract. In our body systems, some of the "garbage" consumed may set off a chain reaction of imbalances like inflammation and stress that can affect the liver, the immune system, the digestive tract, and joints. The more stress on the GI tract, the less time the body has to heal and repair. The essence of whole food is in reducing stress to the body system at large, particularly the GI tract, along with providing the nutrients and co-factors necessary for joint health and mobility.

The major players: sulfur, glucosamine sulfate, and free radicals

In general, the element sulfur is becoming more widely appreciated as a critical nutrient, and is now considered an integral part of maintaining the structural integrity of connective tissues, cartilage, nails, skin, hair, certain enzymes, hormones, antioxidants, and immunoglobulins. Sulfur has anti-inflammatory properties, and some studies even suggest it may provide some analgesic effect on pain relief.

Glucosamine sulfate is made when the body combines sulfur with the amino acid glutamine and a sugar molecule. Glucosamine sulfate's primary biological role is being an essential substrate for the biosynthesis of the glycosaminoglycans, and the hyaluronic acid backbone needed for the formation of the proteoglycans found in the structural matrix of joints. Long story short, if the body does not have enough glutamine or sulfur, it cannot make critically important glucosamine sulfate.

Free radicals are unstable molecules that cause inflammation, stiffness, and pain in joints. Antioxidants bind with free radicals and control oxidative stress and inflammation. Potent antioxidants include vitamin A and the carotenoids, vitamin C, vitamin E, the polyphenols, and the minerals zinc, copper, and selenium.

Supporting joint health through food

Reducing inflammation, reducing free radical damage, and supporting the body's ability to make its own glucosamine sulfate can be supported with whole food and the diet a horse consumes.

The first step is cutting down or eliminating processed sugars. These include the molasses, cane sugar, dextrose, and sucrose often added to supplements. These kinds of sugars can aggravate and increase the inflammatory response. I also recommend caution with grain or grain byproduct carbohydrates, which can also increase inflammation in some horses.

Omega-3 fatty acids are very helpful in reducing chronic inflammation. **Flax and chia seeds** are both excellent sources of omega-3s, as is **pasture grass**. Commercial feeds will often have an inverted ratio of omega-6 to omega-3, so it is important to know what the particular ratio is in the feed you are using. If necessary, you can add flax or chia to the feed to balance the ratio. Chia seeds prove to be fantastic joint supplements because chia is high in the amino acids proline and lysine. Proline and lysine are both needed to make collagen, which helps to heal cartilage and cushion the joints and vertebrae. Note that chia seeds from Ecuador and Bolivia are very high in boron and strontium—important trace minerals that have been leached from the soils in North America. Boron has been shown to reduce the excretion of calcium, and to increase the absorption of calcium, magnesium, and potassium. Strontium is believed to be increase bone formation, bone mass, and strength.

Cabbage is high in the amino acid glutamine, which the body needs to make glucosamine sulfate. In addition, it can provide vitamin C, copper, and selenium. Feed ¼ to ½ cup per day, and remember that horses prefer cabbage chopped, not fed as whole leaves. Freeze-dried and dehydrated cabbage can be fed as an alternative to fresh.

Kale is high in sulfur which the body uses to make glucosamine sulfate, and helps support connective tissue and cartilage. Kale is also high in the antioxidants vitamin A, vitamin C, and copper. Feed ¼ to ½ cup per day, chopped, not whole. Freeze-dried and dehydrated kale can be fed as an alternative to fresh.

Alfalfa is another high-sulfur source. It provides the antioxidants vitamin A, vitamin C, vitamin E, and zinc. Please take note that alfalfa has become a major GMO crop. If your horse has chronic joint issues, it would be best to feed an organic source of alfalfa.

Pomegranates (food-processed, including the peel) and **strawberries** (highly sprayed fruits—wash thoroughly or buy organic) are among the phytonutrient foods that provide anti-inflammatory action in the body. A study of the inflammatory benefits of pomegranates, published in 2009, highlights that pomegranate reduces the production of pro-inflammatory cytokines *interleukin-6* and *interleukin-8*. These particular cytokines contribute to painful joint damage and chronic inflammation.

Other antioxidant foods that should absolutely be fed and enjoyed in the pursuit of better joint health include **blueberries**, **oranges** (with peel for higher amounts of bioflavonoids), **almonds** (sliced or ground), **mangoes** (without the pit), **blackberries, pears, carrots, sunflower seeds, nutritional yeast**, specific **medicinal mushrooms**, and **apples.**

Among the best anti-inflammatory foods are **flax, chia, turmeric, boswellia** (also known as frankincense), **bromelain** (an enzyme from pineapple), **hemp seed oil**, and **oregano.**

Osteoarthritis and circulation

Studies show that 60 percent of all equine lameness is related to osteoarthritis—a result of the physical breakdown of articular cartilage that can affect any horse at any age. It can be the result of repeated cycles of athletic trauma, inflammation of the lining of the joint and the capsule, normal aging process, or osteochondrosis (OCD). Osteoarthritis is not curable, but it is manageable.

Movement is critical to joint health and dealing with osteoarthritis. Circulation is the body's way of sending specific nutrients and co-factors to areas that need support. Specific foods that increase nitric oxide, the master circulatory molecule in the body, can be extremely helpful in increasing joint health and mobility. These foods include **nutritional yeast, oranges, Indian gooseberry, pumpkin seeds**, and **sesame seeds**. Other foods with vasodilating activity (increasing blood flow) include **ginger, parsley, jiaogulan,** and **schisandra.**

Supporting joint health through supplements

Whole food supplements are readily available that will provide cabbage, kale, chia, strawberry and pomegranate for total joint support, as well as nutritional yeast, oranges, pumpkin seeds, sesame seeds, and ginger root powder for increased circulation.

Note that the glucosamine sulfate used in most commercial supplements is derived from shellfish and very unstable, requiring the addition of stabilizers. These are commonly sodium chloride or potassium chloride, which can end up being 30 percent of glucosamine by weight. This means that if a product label says 3,000 milligrams of glucosamine sulfate, you must subtract 900 milligrams (30 percent) to know the actual amount of glucosamine you are feeding.

Diet and joint injections

You can extend the life of common equine joint injections with diet. I have found that horses that have been injected routinely twice a year can begin going a year or more on a single injection. This is because a whole food diet puts less stress on the GI tract, providing the body with more time to heal and repair. Remember, stress reduces available healing time, and the body can only repair and heal when it is at rest and not overworking to digest processed feed.

Why MSM is not a food

Methylsulfonylmethane (MSM) is sulfur-rich compound commonly found in commercial joint supplements. It is a natural substance created when phytoplankton from the oceans decomposes and releases compounds to the atmosphere which react with oxygen and sunlight to produce the final product. Plants and animals take in sulfur by using the MSM and other sulfur compounds that come from the atmosphere. However, the MSM used in most equine joint supplements is made from petroleum waste and methane gas. It is not harvested from the ocean or the atmosphere, making the bioavailability vastly different. Because of this, the better route is to provide your animals with a potent whole-food plant source of sulfur: kale. By incorporating organic kale, we not only provide sulfur, but also the vitamins A, C, K, fiber, carotenoids, flavonoids, calcium, magnesium, manganese, and copper.

Feeding for Healthy Hooves

Over the course of my lifetime, I have had horses with great feet, and horses whose feet nearly drove me into debt trying to fix them. You name the hoof supplement, I've probably used it—in addition to the usual hoof oils, creams, salves, and pine tar. By complete happenstance, before I started BioStar, I began feeding flax seeds to one horse whose coat quality I wanted to improve. This horse also happened to have shelly, brittle, thin-walled feet. After two months, my farrier commented on the improved hoof quality; never did I imagine that flax seed would improve his feet!

Thus began my research into how omega-3s might play a role in healthy hooves. The equine digestive system evolved to process small, continuous meals of vegetation eaten by animals who roam many miles each day, eating all day long. The grasses not only provided water, protein, carbohydrates and fiber, but also fatty acids: high amounts of omega-3 and low amounts of omega-6. Along with diet factors, circulation to the feet was further increased by the fact that these early horses were moving constantly—up to 20 miles per day by some estimates.

The grain connection

Horses need higher amounts of omega-3 than omega-6. When we feed grains (corn, barley, oats, wheat middlings, wheat bran, rice bran, sunflower seeds), we are feeding higher amounts of omega-6. Additional sources of omega-3 like flax or chia seed must be added to maintain an omega-3:omega-6 ratio of at least 2.5:1. That's a minimum ratio, by the way;

some researchers are now making a case for increased ratios of up to 4:1 omega 3 to omega 6.

Grasses and hay do provide omega-3s, although the omega-3 content in hay can be severely affected by how it was stored and maintained. I personally don't depend on hay for omega-3s. Ten to twelve hours of turnout on grass, per day, will elevate the important omega-3s in the equine diet, although this too can be affected by the type of grass. Coastal or bahia grasses, for example, don't have the omega-3 content of timothy, blue grass or orchard grasses.

Protein and the amino acids

The hoof wall is made up of approximately 93 percent protein, which is built from amino acids. Hooves contain the amino acids cysteine, arginine, leucine, lysine, proline, serine, glycine, valine, methionine, phenylalanine and histidine. Diets that are deficient in one or more of these can lead to reduced hoof growth. Most of the hoof wall is composed of an insoluble protein called keratin, which includes the amino acids glycine, phenylalanine, arginine, cysteine and proline. Of these, cysteine is especially important, as it makes up approximately 24 percent of keratin. Another sulfur-containing amino acid, methionine, can be readily converted by the body into cysteine. Good food sources for methionine include sesame seeds, eggs, oats, wheat germ, and almonds. Many commercial hoof supplements, however, provide a synthetic form of this compound listed as "DL-methionine" on the label. While providing methionine for conversion to cysteine does make nutritional sense, this rationale ignores the other key amino acids in keratin: glycine, phenylalanine, proline, and arginine. Including one important amino acid—and ignoring the rest—

may explain in part why some hoof supplements that contain methionine tend to work for some horses, but not for others. Foods such as alfalfa, hemp protein, egg protein and whey protein are good sources of all five of these amino acids.

Zinc and copper

Copper is essential to healthy hooves, as it is part of an enzyme required for creating the disulfide bonds that hold keratin together. The element is also needed by another copper-dependent enzyme responsible for the structural integrity of collagen. Zinc is present in high concentrations in normal hoof tissue, as it also plays a role in enzymatic action and the formation of keratin and collagen. A zinc deficiency can reveal itself in slow hoof growth, thin walls, white line, and abscesses.

Excess iron can interfere with both zinc and copper metabolism, but it should be noted that iron absorption is low in equines `), while zinc's absorption range is 5 percent to 90 percent. Similarly, excess amounts of calcium from foods like alfalfa hay can negatively impact the absorption of zinc. Horses that get alfalfa hay only (and no other hay mix, like orchard or timothy) may need supplemental zinc.

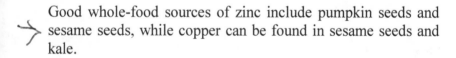

Good whole-food sources of zinc include pumpkin seeds and sesame seeds, while copper can be found in sesame seeds and kale.

Biotin

Most hoof supplements provide the B-vitamin biotin. Only a handful of studies have been performed to determine the effect of biotin in horses, and the most recent one was in 1998. A

Swiss study (1995) and a South African study (1992) highlight that biotin supplementation will not produce results over a 30-day period. Both studies were much longer—nine months in duration—and only the South African study demonstrated improved hoof growth on 15 mg of biotin per day. The Swiss study, based on 20 mg of biotin per day, showed no improvement of hoof growth when compared to a control group without any biotin supplementation. If you choose to feed a hoof supplement containing biotin, it is important to give the product a good 7 to 9 months, because it takes time to see if your horse's feet will benefit. Whole food sources of biotin include nutritional yeast, rice, sunflower seeds, and mushrooms.

Colostrum

With over 70 different growth factors in bovine colostrum, this whole food can be very helpful in building better feet. One reason for colostrum's effectiveness is that these growth factors help stimulate cellular reproduction and regulate roles in cell growth, encouraging normal growth as well as the healing and repair of tissues. Colostrum is one of my "go to" foods when dealing with hoof growth and hoof integrity issues.

Soy

Soy has a high phytic acid content, which can prevent zinc, copper, magnesium, and iron from being absorbed properly in the GI tract. If your horse has weak, shelly feet, it might be best to avoid soy.

Circulation is key

The strength of the equine foot depends on nourishment that begins with good circulation and vascularity. Arteries, veins, and capillaries are vascular pathways that deliver nutrients and oxygen through bone and soft tissue, and are key elements in providing hoof support and maintaining hoof health. Poor circulation in the feet will most certainly affect the quality of the hoof wall. How do we improve circulation? Movement plays a huge role, and remember, horses are designed to be on the move. The trouble is, 24-hour turnout in a big pasture where the horse is constantly moving and grazing is not possible for many horses in boarding and training barns, or even for many horses kept at home.

In response, many training barns in Europe and the US use mechanical horse walkers to offer more exercise and thus better circulation for horses with limited turnout. Treadmills like those sold by Horse Gym are also becoming more common. Some riders take their horses out twice per day, starting with a training session in the morning and then an afternoon hack or walk. Not only is this good for building muscle and fitness, but it's also very good for increasing circulation to the feet. Even hand walking, several times per day on grassy and hard surfaces, will increase circulation to the feet and help support healthy hooves.

Further thoughts on hoof health

There are many factors that affect hoof growth and hoof quality: age, breed, genetics, exercise, nutritional influences and or imbalances, environment, illness, shoeing, trimming, and metabolic disorders. Not all of these factors are under our control, but many of them are. Nutrition, circulation, and good farrier care are all critical elements to the long-term maintenance of healthy feet. Personally, I've adopted a less-is-more approach to equine hoof health and general well-being that can be summarized in several points:

- Horses need mostly fibrous foods: pasture, forage, and hay.
- They need higher amounts of omega-3 than omega-6. Adding chia seeds or flax seeds is particularly important for horses that are stalled with limited turnout, or those living in drought pastures or pastures with bahia or coastal grasses.
- They need good, quality protein like alfalfa pellets or cubes to provide all of the amino acids they require.
- They need mineral support from salt licks or free-choice mineral salts, and a multi-vitamin/mineral supplement.
- Circulation is critical to healthy hooves, and good circulation means movement. Horses are by nature grazers, and they need to move and eat 20 hours a day. Supplements that contain arginine for stimulating production of nitric oxide, the master circulatory molecule in the body, can also be very beneficial to increasing circulation to the feet.

Feeding for Recovery

Human athletes are well known for taking steps to ensure optimal recovery after grueling workouts. Performance and sport horses are athletes in every sense of the word. Like their human counterparts, equine athletes train rigorously and sometimes compete in less-than-optimal conditions: high heat, humidity, unsure footing, high winds, and torrential downpours. Add to this the stress exerted on equine athletes from shipping and competing in unfamiliar venues. Beyond that, as if their own stressors weren't enough, horses are often affected by the stress of the humans and other horses around them.

Physical and mental stress impacts the digestive system, the immune system, and the glandular system at large, particularly the adrenals, thyroid, and liver. The result of all this stress can cause digestive upset, muscle fatigue, inflammation, lowered resistance to bacteria and viruses, an overstimulated immune system, and oxidative stress. Excessive or constant stresses can eventually result in an unhealthy triad called subclinical musculoskeletal trauma: the combination of muscle damage, inflammation and oxidative stress. This can play a huge role in lackluster performance and recurring soreness and fatigue.

First things first

For horses, the best place to start with recovery feeding is hay. You don't want to feed too high a protein content for recovery (no straight alfalfa hay), so a timothy or an orchard grass, or even timothy or orchard mixed with alfalfa would be best. For further hydration, soaked alfalfa cubes or pellets are a good choice because they are lower in protein than straight alfalfa hay. As long as the horse is not metabolic, you can add a banana, a chopped orange or a kiwi. Adding a fruit carbohydrate will assist in the glycogen reloading—just like these same recovery foods benefit human athletes. It's best not to feed concentrates, grains, or processed feeds for at least one hour after the horse has been given its hay and fruit for recovery.

Four pillars of recovery

To understand why the best equine recovery foods work, it helps to know the four basic factors that most strongly determine the body's ability to recover from daily training: sugar, salt, water, and rest.

The body uses **sugar** (glucose and fructose) for muscle glycogen, liver glycogen, and blood sugar. To fuel the muscles during exercise, the body uses muscle glycogen and very little blood sugar. The longer the training session, the more muscle glycogen is depleted and the more the body turns to its blood sugar store. Of the glucose that is initially stored as glycogen and then converted for use, 75 percent is directed to the brain and related central nervous system functions. The remaining 25 percent is used for production of red blood cells, skeletal muscle, and heart muscle.

Elite human athletes—and by extension, equine athletes—can benefit from using specific fruits (bananas, dates, oranges) to replenish glycogen supplies after training. Fruit sources also provide enzymes, some B vitamins, fiber, a little protein, and water. With fruit carbohydrates, the timing is critical: they must be eaten 30 minutes to one hour after cool-down because these carbohydrates have been shown to speed recovery, and this time frame represents the muscles' peak period for glycogen reloading. When fruit carbohydrates are combined with some protein, increased glycogen reloading occurs. Based on studies published in the *Journal of Applied Physiology*, the carb/protein combination increased glycogen reloading by 38 percent over carbohydrates alone. Be careful, though—too much protein can have the opposite effect.

Salt plays a role in virtually every function of the cell and the homeostasis of mineral salts is essential: too much and we increase dehydration; too little and many body functions cease to work properly. Sodium and potassium are two of the key minerals involved in electrolyte balance. Sodium can be thought of as the extracellular mineral, while potassium is the intracellular mineral. To maintain the body's acid/alkaline balance, alkaline minerals must be available to neutralize the acidic byproducts of metabolism and physical activity. Chlorine, sulfur, and phosphorus are the acidic minerals, while calcium, magnesium, sodium, and potassium are the alkaline minerals. Most equine electrolyte supplements use sodium chloride, which has been processed to remove the alkaline minerals. Its pH is 7.0, which is neutral. Celtic sea salt, Redmond salt and Himalayan salt provide the acidic and alkaline mineral blend for a final pH of around 8.0 (slightly alkaline), which helps to rebalance the acidic byproducts of metabolism and physical activity.

We all know how important **hydration** is to any kind of recovery. With that in mind, feeding a wet feed can be very helpful in maintaining full hydration for your horse, along with water buckets. A half cup or so of Guinness Stout beer at night can also help with appetite and hydration.

Rest includes sleep, naturally, but also the absence of stress. Refined foods, processed foods, and supplements from non-food sources can increase digestive stress, thus slowing the rate of recovery. Quality forage, access to grazing, and whole food (and whole recovery food supplements) can encourage the most rapid recovery. A reminder: show grounds can contribute to increased stress, so it's important when you do night check to be as quiet and respectful to all the horses as possible…they need their rest.

Free radicals and glutathione

Oxygen provides energy to sustain life. The ability to absorb it, transport it and use it is essential for equine athletes. However, the oxygen molecule we all breathe is a double-edged sword. In harnessing the chemical energy of oxygen, cellular havoc can ensue by means of transient, highly reactive, potentially destructive molecules called free radicals.

On the atomic level, electrons are only stable when paired with a partner, which is why molecules that are stable and nonreactive have chemical bonds containing a pair of shared electrons. Free radicals are unpaired; they are desperate to snatch electrons from other chemical bonds around them. Free radical chain reactions are fast, lasting for perhaps 100 millionth of a second before snatching back an electron from another chemical bond. Problems arise when electrons are ripped out of the chemical bonds that hold important structures together—like cell walls or DNA. Irreparable damage to the cell and its genetic material may be the result. Free radicals can attack lipid membranes around cells, forming damaging peroxides, which are not produced in other metabolic pathways. This damage, known as oxidative stress, is thought to be one of the root causes of degenerative diseases, inflammation, and aging itself.

Free radicals are produced during cellular metabolism, and increase during exercise. These free radicals react within cells in a process called oxidation that can result in inflammation accumulation. Over time this inflammation decreases functional efficiency of the cell and contributes to oxidative stress.

To fight this cellular destruction, the body uses a master antioxidant called *glutathione peroxidase*. Glutathione plays another important role: antioxidant cycling. Glutathione has a synergistic relationship with several key antioxidants including vitamin E, vitamin C, and the enzyme Q10. Antioxidant cycling is the process of antioxidants extending other antioxidants' lives, making them more effective. When glutathione converts other antioxidants back to their functional forms, it loses an electron and becomes ineffective. The body then needs to synthesize more glutathione, and for this it needs an important co-factor: the amino acid cysteine.

Bovine colostrum provides both glutathione and cysteine to ensure that proper levels of this cellular antioxidant can be replenished and that antioxidant cycling can be maintained. This enables the body to reduce the harmful levels of oxidative stress and damage caused by the free radicals that build up during exercise.

Other powerful antioxidants include...

- Vitamin E, which extends protection to cell membranes and fats under threat of damaging oxidation reactions.

Good sources of vitamin E include almonds and wheat germ.

- Flavonoids, which are capable of cellular damage repair and found in high amounts in almonds and pomegranates.
- Polyphenol antioxidants, which affect cell-to-cell signaling, receptor sensitivity, inflammatory enzyme activity, and gene regulation. Polyphenol antioxidants can also protect nitric oxide—critical to circulation— against oxidative destruction, and are found in a variety of whole foods including fruits and legumes.

The mineral connection

Due to nutrient deficiencies in soils all over the United States, providing adequate mineral content in a horse recovery supplement has become even more critical. From transporting oxygen, to the growth, maintenance and repair of tissues and bones, to minimizing fatigue, minerals—particularly calcium, magnesium, iron, potassium, selenium, sodium, zinc and the trace minerals—are extremely important to the equine athlete. Silica clay helps to bind and absorb oxidative damage toxins and heavy metals from the GI tract. Silica is also an important nutrient for maintenance of connective tissue, skin, and hair.

In addition to recovery feeding, recovery supplements can be used as needed, during competitions and shipping, during days of hard training, or every day if desired.

Feeding for the Metabolic Horse

Over the past several years, as the number of metabolic horses has increased to almost epidemic proportions, I have been diligently studying, testing, and experimenting with plants and foods to see what can help bring balance to the metabolic horse's system. Every time a new supplement comes out for insulin resistant or Cushing's horses with these endocrine disorders, I immediately go and read the labeled ingredients. Then I either think to myself, "Hmm, I need to do some research on that ingredient," or often, when I'm already familiar with the ingredient, "Why would a company include that?"

Of course, the fundamentals for maintaining a healthy horse with metabolic issues (or one that could become metabolic) begin with what the horse eats and how it lives, so this is the perfect place to start.

Food and Lifestyle

While low carbohydrate feeds and ration balancers have become popular, I have found that simplicity, combined with real whole food, is the best course for most metabolic horses. Real food does not stress the GI tract as highly processed feeds do, and real food provides the matrix of nutritional factors which food byproducts don't.

What's more, I don't think there is much doubt that rich pastures contribute to metabolic diseases and overweight horses. The grass seeds commonly available for horse pastures are designed to fatten cows. The chemical fertilizers (nitrogen, phosphorus, potassium), which are petroleum based, end up stripping the soil of its health and contaminating ground water. There is growing evidence that these synthetic chemical fertilizers seriously deplete the nutritional content of foods. Having a good long term plan for restoration of native grasses and herbs and some old-fashioned manure-spreading is a good start to returning health to the soil and health to our horses. At the very least, avoid chemical fertilizers and the herbicides glyphosate and 2-4D.

Exercise and movement

The horses on my farm live predominately in a herd situation. They move from one end of a very large pasture to the other, up and down hills, into creeks, occasionally kicking up their heels for a race to the pond. They may be retired from competition, but they are still active. Metabolic horses kept in stalls with limited turnout pose a challenge, because movement and exercise is critically important in the management of this disease. The dilemma is that horses need to eat 20 hours a day but, just as importantly, they need to move around. It turns out that Eastern medicine provides a unique approach to balancing metabolism.

The Ayurvedic Approach

In Ayurvedic and traditional Chinese medicine, the focus on wellness is a focus on balance—that is, balancing the body system at large. A metabolic imbalance, for instance, can cause a cascade of other imbalances: liver, GI tract and immune system, as well as increased inflammation. In Ayurvedic medicine (see Appendix F) there are three energetic principles that govern physiological activity, known as *doshas*. The word *dosha* literally means, "that which changes." The *doshas* govern movement and blood flow, metabolism, digestion, heat, structure, vitality, and fluid balance in the body. Specific foods and herbs used in Ayurvedic medicine are called *tridoshic*, meaning balancing for all three *doshas*. These distinct plants and foods help to re-calibrate and re-harmonize the body system.

How do Ayurvedic principles apply to metabolic horses? We know that one body system out of balance causes other body system imbalances. We know that when we try to re-balance one element, we frequently cause something else to get thrown out of whack. The Ayurvedic approach is to focus on the whole horse. In the spirit of Ayurveda, I came up with a *tridoshic* formula that encompasses cortisol reduction, liver support, immune support, fat metabolism, and reduced inflammation. Since its genesis, that formula has gone through many changes, tweaks, adjustments, multiple laboratory analyses, and a variety of test horses. Formulating of this type is part science, part intuition, and part what the horses have to say and show me in terms of how an ingredient or a formula is working. So far, so good.

East meets West

Complimentary foods and minerals based on what we know of Western medicine provide important support to metabolic horses and easy keepers. This *tridoshic* recipe is a true blend of East and West, including amino-acid-chelated magnesium, which is a more bioavailable form than magnesium found in oxides or sulfates. Carnitine, a dipeptide, is important for energy metabolism due to its fat-burning capabilities. There is also gamma–linolenic acid (GLA) that provides the body with what it needs to regulate inflammation. Rounding out the ingredients list are: organic amalaki (Indian gooseberry), organic holy basil, organic chasteberry, organic schisandra, organic milk thistle, organic fenugreek seeds, organic hemp seed fines, almond flour, and organic spirulina.

While this is a nearly all-inclusive recipe, it's not quite. To be effective, the *tridoshic* needs to be accompanied by a couple of additional ingredients: chia seeds, which help slow the digestion of carbohydrates; and the mineral chromium—in particular the glucose-tolerance factor (GTF) chromium provided in large amounts by brewer's yeast and nutritional yeast.

Feeding for the Hindgut Ulcer Horse

Hindgut ulcer development and hindgut acidosis have become almost as prevalent as gastric ulcers in horses. Causes behind colonic ulcers include the use of NSAIDs (particularly Bute and Banamine), acidity of the hindgut being increased (specifically by large quantities of undigested starches and sugars reaching the hindgut and producing lactic acid), stress (mental or physical, which releases corticosteroids that inhibit the specific anti-inflammatory prostaglandins), and long term daily use of omeprazole.

Common medications for hindgut ulcers include sucralfate and misoprostol. Sucralfate binds to the ulcer bed and forms a kind of bandage over the ulcer. It has also shown that it can stimulate a cytoprotective (cell-protecting) effect on the colon mucosa. Misoprostol is a synthetic prostaglandin (a hormone-like substance) that protects mucosa by increasing mucus production and regulating inflammation.

Feeding during treatment

It is important during the healing and recovery period that the hindgut is allowed to "rest". This means reducing hay, which by its fibrous nature is harder to digest, putting more stress on the hindgut. Substitute soaked hay cubes (timothy/alfalfa) for hay flakes, thus providing the much needed fiber in an easy-to-digest form. Provide soaked hay cubes every two hours if the horse is stalled, and if needed, a flake of hay can be given at the night-check feeding along with another bucket of soaked hay cubes. Allow the horse to hand-graze several times a day if the horse has no access to pasture and grazing. Access to adequate pasture can replace some of the frequent soaked hay cube meals. On average, a horse will need to be on the soaked cube program for at least 30 days. After a favorable follow-up ultrasound, hay can gradually be re-introduced and the soaked cubes reduced.

Consider reducing grain concentrates, and adding molasses-free **beet pulp** (use Speedi-Beet if you want to avoid GMOs). Add some whole **flax seed** or stabilized flax for additional Omega 3's, and some **alfalfa or timothy pellets** for added easy-to-digest fiber and protein. For additional fat sources, **coconut meal or rice bran** can be added.

Yeast probiotics are important for fiber digestion and fermentation. However, in a hindgut ulcer horse, there is already inflammation (heat) and yeasts by their nature are "heating" or "warming" elements. I like to recommend starting with **cooling probiotics**: the *Lactobacillus* family, abbreviated on labels as "L." It is also important to include mannan oligosaccharides (MOS) which helps to regulate the pH of the hindgut.

Hemp seed oil contains GLA (gamma-linolenic acid) which the body can use to regulate the prostaglandins and decrease inflammation. It is particularly beneficial for horses who begin to transition off of misoprostol because hemp seed oil continues to support the reduction of inflammation.

Stalled horse stress

One of the lesser-discussed issues with horses that are stalled is that they are not in physical contact with other horses. They are confined to a stall, and confined to a turn-out paddock by themselves. We know this is not a normal living situation for a grazing herd animal. Horses who live in groups or get turned out with a buddy will share neck-scratching duties, sometimes grazing close together or standing side-by-side for a snooze in the sun. Even with a pristine paddock and beautiful barn/stall set up with close attention paid to every horse, the lack of physical contact with other equines can cause chronic stress. Some horses can adapt to the isolation, while others can't. Chronic stress leads to ulcer issues, and many times it is hard to evaluate an individual horse's stress levels—particularly the stoic ones.

Quantity and quality

What and how we feed is vitally important: quality of hay, quality of forage, quality of feed and quality of water. As owners and riders we always need to ask ourselves, "Is this feed, this supplement, this hay going to decrease stress on the GI tract or increase it?"

Feeding grain concentrates three or four times per day is far better for the health and functioning of the GI tract than feeding them twice per day. Horses need to eat hay or graze twenty hours per day. Any fasting time lasting longer than four hours is a recipe for increased stress.

Reducing hindgut ulcer recurrence

Yeast probiotics are specific to the digestion of fiber in the hindgut and are important for hindgut fermentation. Only live/viable yeast probiotics (those that are labeled with CFUs) are capable of colonization. Make sure the CFUs are at least 100 billion per serving.

Adaptogenic herbs are also beneficial to reducing stress. These include **ginseng, ashwaganda,** and **holy basil**, which have shown to reduce cortisol. Yeast probiotics are not recommended if a horse has an active hindgut ulcer or acidosis (see "Feeding during treatment" above).

Whether you're dealing with a hindgut ulcer horse or not, keeping human stress in check is also important in reducing stress in horses. Horses can read us like books, and some will start stressing because their owner is stressing, or the groom is stressing, or the trainer is stressing, or the barn manager is stressing. It's always a good idea to keep the barn a drama-free zone.

Feeding for Lyme Disease Support / EPM Support

Most of what we hear about Lyme disease focuses on the danger to humans, but our equine companions are even more at risk. Timely diagnosis and treatment of Lyme disease in horses is essential. Together with drug therapies, it's also crucially important to provide the strong, consistent nutritional support they need for physical and mental well-being on the way to recovery.

Lyme disease earned its name from the Connecticut community where it was first detected in humans in 1975. By 2006, Lyme had become the most common tick-borne illness in the United States. Doxycycline is commonly prescribed, but the price of this antibiotic has skyrocketed a few years ago from $36 per bottle to upwards of $400—a faster rise than any other generic drug at the time. Tetracycline, also used in treatment, has escalated in price as well, along with minocycline, which is only somewhat less expensive.

Elements of Lyme: Inflammation, the immune system, and relapse

One of the benefits of doxycycline is its ability to reduce inflammation. Frequently, NSAIDs are additionally prescribed during treatment. When the body system is infected with Lyme disease, the causative bacteria (*Borrelia burgdorferi*) can use evasion tactics by going dormant and hidden inside the cell. It can then re-enter the joint at a later stage, after antibiotic therapy is completed. Although some horses will relapse due to reinfection from another tick bite, many times the relapse is simply because the bacteria has managed to hide in the body and then re-emerge.

Less sugar, more exercise

Sugar can feed the *Borellia* spirochetes, particular refined sugars like molasses, sucrose, or dextrose. It's best to avoid feeding wheat because it metabolizes to sugar very quickly in the body. Check your supplement labels, as supplements often have added dextrose or molasses for palatability. Fruits like carrots, apples, blueberries, and papaya are fine in small quantities.

It is important that the horse get exercise because it supports the immune functions, and helps to regulate the body's inflammatory response. Another added benefit to exercise is that it can improve emotional and mental health by increasing endorphin production.

Nutritional support during treatment

Taking care of the microbiome of the GI tract is imperative with all antibiotic treatments. Generally, it is advised to stay on **probiotics** for several months following antibiotic therapy. It is important to not give the probiotics at the same time as the antibiotics, but timed at least one to two hours (or more) after antibiotic administration.

Along with probiotics, **bovine colostrum** is a unique, supportive food rich in immunoglobulins. It provides specific proline-rich polypeptides (PRPs) to regulate the thymus, the master gland of the immune system. Another benefit of bovine colostrum is in the high concentrations of epidermal growth factor (EGF) and betacellulin (BTC) it contains, which can reduce gastrointestinal damage by promoting cell growth.

Medicinal mushrooms can also be used for immune support during Lyme disease treatment, as they are capable of regulating the immune response by providing a diverse class of compounds known as polysaccharide immunomodulators. Like all fungi, these mushrooms produce various antiviral, antibacterial, and antimicrobial compounds to survive in the wild against pathogenic or competing organisms. Fungi lack immune systems, so these compounds are their defense. The antibiotic penicillin, and the antifungal drug griseofulvin are both produced by the fungus. The most studied and promising medicinal mushrooms for the immune system are turkey tail, reishi, maitake, and cordycepts.

Kale and chia seeds are supportive of collagen, one of the tissues damaged by the *Borrelia* spirochete. Kale does this by providing vitamin C, and chia seeds are high in the amino acid proline (a major constituent of collagen) and beneficial omega-3 fatty acids. **Bovine colostrum** also provides the transforming growth factors TgF A & B, which promote cell proliferation and tissue repair.

Antioxidant and anti-inflammatory support

Glutathione protects cells and mitochondria from oxidative damage caused by Lyme disease and supports liver health. Quality **un-denatured whey protein** provides the key amino acids for glutathione production and a unique form of cysteine that is highly bioactive for conversion to glutathione.

Turmeric and boswellia play important roles in the regulation of inflammation and provide analgesic benefits. This is important for the joint and body soreness in horses that is associated with Lyme disease. Turmeric can also increase cellular glutathione, thereby increasing antioxidant support.

More about what to feed and when to supplement

Lyme disease increases stress on the body system, while the antibiotic therapies can add to the problem by irritating and upsetting the GI tract. Horses with compromised immune systems benefit from a GMO-free diet and low-to-zero exposure to herbicides, particularly glyphosate. It is recommended that horses have access to hay or pasture for at least 20 hours per day. If feeding a commercial feed, we recommend adding some organic alfalfa pellets or cubes for additional protein, fiber and calcium. Timothy pellets can also be used. Supportive foods such as chopped kale, almonds, pumpkin seeds and adaptogenic herbs like holy basil or ashwaganda can also be fed in small quantities.

As soon as your horse has been diagnosed with Lyme, start on a probiotic, along with chia seeds and colostrum. Three to four weeks later, add antioxidants, turmeric and boswellia. For horses, medicinal mushrooms and holy basil can be fed at the beginning of treatment or at the end of treatment to provide stress relief, liver support, and immune support.

The Road Less Traveled

I shall be telling this with a sigh
Somewhere ages and ages hence:
Two roads diverged in a wood, and I—
I took the one less traveled by,
And that has made all the difference.

-Robert Frost

That summer afternoon when I read the labeled ingredients on the feed bag, I was at a fork in the road: stay with commercial feeds or take the path of the unknown and make the feed myself. Of course I had trepidation. I didn't have a Ph.D. in equine nutrition, and the feed companies had pretty much convinced me that I couldn't feed my horses without them. But I kept thinking back to my forebears who fed their horses with food, real food...why couldn't I?

I will admit that some of my friends thought I'd gone off my rocker, gone around the bend, and fallen into the abyss of earth muffin-ness.

Looking back to that fork in the road now, ten years later, I can say that the road less traveled may be in fact the most rewarding road I've taken. Not only have the horses benefitted, but so have my dogs, as well as my own awareness of what I eat: what it is, how it is grown, where it comes from. My farm has benefited because the manure I compost is of such high quality. What I put back into the earth benefits the ecosystem of plants and soil.

Among the unexpected gifts of this path have been the horses and people I have come to know. Every horse is my teacher and some have wielded the proverbial headmaster's wooden cane to keep me humble, to keep me learning, to keep me paying attention. Ultimately that's what a road less traveled is: learning, growing, empowering, and giving. On the whole food road, the results are health, well-being, and the light in our horses' eyes.

Appendices

APPENDIX A

An Ode to Dirt

Dirt. Horses and dogs love to roll in it, plants need to grow in it, and children like to make mud pies out of it. We get dirt under our fingernails, on our clothes, and all over our hands. We do not typically subscribe to the wonderful attributes of dirt; in fact, oftentimes we disparage it. But the more I learn about dirt, the more fascinating I find dirt to be. In fact, did you know that dirt is one of the fundamental keys to health, performance, and well-being? It is at the crux of GI tract health, as well as the immune, bone, and muscle systems.

Because of the rather derogatory associations we make with dirt, let's instead call it what it really is: soil. Basic elements like carbon and nitrogen, along with climate adjustments, weather, decayed plants and animals, volcanoes, and retreating oceans have all combined over millions of years to make up soil. And within this mix of humus, clay, sand and minerals are species older than dinosaurs: microbes, bacteria, and fungi. Nutrition starts in the ground, and soil becomes the cradle of minerals and the microscopic nutrients that the plant uses to form phytonutrients. It is these phytonutrients that are essential in building the plant's immune system. Phytonutrients are also the building blocks of flavor. This does not mean sweetness. It means subtle, complex flavors that create many tones—think wine, chocolate, coffee and similar foods and beverages, where you can taste individual nuances among varieties.

The root systems of plants create mini-highways in the soil allowing the soil organisms to move around. Unhealthy soils that are compacted or too dry do not have the space for air to circulate, for the roots to spread, or for the microorganisms to move. Much of the nutrient cycling and disease suppression needed by plants occurs in this area known as the *rhizosphere*. Symbiotic funguses in healthy soil bring minerals to the plant: calcium, phosphorus, magnesium, manganese, copper, zinc, selenium, iron, boron, etc. These minerals are essential to health for humans, horses, and dogs. So why do commercial feeds need to be fortified with these and other minerals? It's because the grains and plant byproducts used in commercial feeds are grown in unhealthy soil; therefore, the mineral uptake is very low to non-existent. Food is only as healthy and nutritious as the soil in which it was grown. Why are hay analyses all over the country showing low levels of key minerals like zinc, copper and almost no traces of boron? Why are magnesium levels often so low? When chemical fertilizers are applied, they are applied in a soluble form which feeds the plant, not the soil. Yet, the soil and its organisms are *key* to nutrient uptake. Adding synthetic nitrogen is like dropping a bomb on the soil microbe community.

There are many reasons why horses must have a multi-mineral supplement. In many places our pasture soil is compacted, or has been sprayed in the past with chemical fertilizers or herbicides, thus reducing plant uptake of minerals. Many farms have stopped spreading manure, and mistakenly have starved the soil of food for the microbes. Horse farms can be fantastic places for composting, but often no composting is done, out of worry over flies or for other reasons. Pasture rotation often can't be accomplished because there are more horses than there are pastures to rotate them on. Processed feeds and complete feeds have the added minerals, often in non-organic forms (carbonates rather than chelates), but few horse owners or barns feed the amount the feed company recommends, thus increasing the potential mineral deficit in the horses' diets.

Hay is frequently grown with chemical fertilizers, which as we know, play havoc with the soil organisms, often killing them off or driving them away. Without the soil organisms, the timothy or orchard grass or alfalfa cannot take up vital minerals and phytonutrients through their root systems. Hay fields are often sprayed with glyphosate (Roundup) which binds important immune system minerals like copper and zinc, thereby giving the weeds an immune deficiency—a plant form of AIDS. More and more hay farms are following Monsanto's advice to use Roundup also as a desiccant two weeks before harvesting to speed up the drying process. Roundup and its inert ingredients can stay in the soil for years, binding key minerals and preventing them from plant uptake.

One of the key qualities that is fundamental to organics is care of the soil. Particularly with biodynamic farming, soil is nurtured just as well as the animals and plants. These farmers can read the soil, tell what is lacking depending on what weed sprouts up from year to year, and how to consistently encourage the healthy soil symbiosis. Plants grown organically and biodynamically will have a greater uptake of minerals and phytonutrients thus making them more nutritious too!

Taking care of our soils is the fundamental first step in fixing our food system. And really when you think about it, there is a kind of coolness factor in realizing how complex, collective, and collaborative the earth is beneath our feet. Make sure your horses are getting the minerals they need from a quality multivitamin/mineral supplement, while we all get to work on nurturing healthy soils.

Biodiversity is good: Portrait of a healthy pasture

Ten years ago, a friend sent me a packet of wildflower seeds, which I indiscriminately sprinkled along the outside of a fence line. My friend had suggested I plant the seeds along the side of the house lawn, but I thought to myself, "Why ruin my lawn?" But when some of those wildflowers actually came up from my haphazard planting, I had an epiphany: These are native plants. Why am I freaking out if I see anything that isn't a grass in my pastures? Then it occurred to me that pastures 100 years ago were not single plant monocultures, but diverse ecosystems.

These days I have cool and warm season grasses (orchard, big bluestem, Indian grass as well as clover and some fescue), wild herbs, and wild flowers growing everywhere: pastures, fence lines, and the grassy area once known as a lawn, which in spring looks more like a dandelion convention. We leave swaths of pasture unmowed along the tree line for the birds, the butterflies, bumblebees and other wild bees. Even the paddocks have wild chamomile growing along some of the fence lines. Blackberry thickets have sprung up, the honeysuckle vines provide food for the hummingbirds, and the elderberries, which I used to hack down as a nuisance, are providing pollen for my neighbor's honeybees.

I have come to appreciate diversity, and in fact seek it.

Diversity and the GI tract

Diversity plays an important role in diet. The microbiome of the gastrointestinal tract is a multi-strain universe that depends on food varieties to support diversity of beneficial microorganisms. Studies of small diet changes in mice and humans show that various colonies of beneficial bacteria can be increased within 24 hours by simply adding a new food to the diet.

Supporting good GI tract microbiome diversity does not mean you have to overhaul your feed program overnight; in fact, doing so could cause an upset in the colonies of the GI tract. Supporting healthy microorganisms in the gut can be as simple as offering your horse small amounts of different foods like cucumbers, celery, squash, lettuce, pumpkin seeds, chopped beet greens, some slices of papaya, mango, a handful of blueberries, some parsley, a few carrot tops, some basil leaves. My horses love mint: spearmint, apple mint, and peppermint leaves from right out of the garden. I also like to rotate hays: alfalfa with timothy, orchard grass with alfalfa, orchard grass and timothy, and sometimes some chaff hay sprinkled in.

There are some wonderful herbs that, if allowed to grow in pastures, provide supplemental variety for horses: chicory, milk thistle, burdock root (horses can dig up the root in winter and eat it), chamomile, dandelions, chickweed, and plantain. Just because these herbs are growing in the pasture does not mean a horse devours them; horses nibble on the herbs and move back to the grasses. What one human might call a weed, another might know as a medicine. Similarly, we've all known horses who will chow down on the dandelions, and others who couldn't be less interested. It is the same with the beneficial wild herbs.

Diversity in the ecosystem

When we look at the ecosystem at large, the sheer diversity of plants, animals, and insects we see only highlights the fact that a monoculture approach works against the very essence of Nature. We need to celebrate diversity, encourage it. We need to consider the other species that do share pastures and trees with us and with the horses. Because all the elements in an ecosystem work together—depend on each other. Think of the diverse populations that comprise the microbiome of the horse's gut as a mirror for the diversity in Nature. Is there only one kind of tree? Only one kind of grass? One kind of wildflower?

I used to look at lovely lush pastures and think, what could be better for horses? But I have since changed my tune. When I see pasture grasses sprinkled with dandelions, clover, some Queen Anne's Lace, some chamomile, I see an ecology-minded pasture that is not only beneficial for the horses, but for the birds, insects, and bees. Diversity is a fundamental component of the natural world. When we fear diversity, we become disconnected, and all the components of the ecosystem are then at risk from the imbalance. Our job is not to conquer the fields. Our job is to harmonize with the fields.

APPENDIX B

Metal toxicity and other environmental contaminants

The past decade has seen a rare type of chronic kidney disease (CKD) kill thousands of agricultural workers along Central America's Pacific coast, in Sri Lanka and in India, with emerging evidence pointing to the widespread use of pesticides and herbicides as a causative factor. An ongoing study conducted with assistance from the Pan American Health Organization, suggests that it may specifically be the heavy metals contained in these pesticides, herbicides, and fertilizers that's to blame; samples of soil and water taken from the El Salvadoran village of Ciudad Romero confirm the presence of high cadmium and arsenic levels.

Organic or not? (Even with arsenic, it matters.)

Arsenic is a "metalloid" element found in organic compounds naturally present in soil, rocks, and water. There is no evidence that arsenic in this form, in small amounts, poses any health risk to animals or humans. Inorganic arsenic, however, is formed when the element bonds with oxygen, chlorine, or sulfur. In this form, arsenic is considered a carcinogen, and has been linked to problems with the GI tract, kidneys, liver, lungs, and skin. Man-made pesticides and herbicides can contain high levels of inorganic arsenic. Eighty percent of the rice in the U.S. comes from the South Central region, grown on lands that have been sprayed with arsenic pesticide to combat cotton boll weevils. As a result, the large rice-growing states in the U.S.— Texas, Louisiana, Mississippi, Missouri, and Florida—have higher inorganic arsenic levels in their rice than rice grown in California. In addition, water runoff from industrialized farming operations where pesticides and herbicides are heavily used is considered a significant contributor to the rise in inorganic arsenic.

A 2013 study published in the *Journal of the American Medical Association* shows that arsenic-tinged rice plants display significant cellular changes that are linked to cancer development. Researchers quantified results in this study by analyzing urine samples of participants for damaged chromosomes no longer able to participate in cell division. In a 2012 *Environmental Health* paper, researchers at the University of California, Davis published the first-ever study on dietary exposure to 11 toxins, including acrylamide, arsenic, lead, mercury, dioxins, DDE, chlordane, and dieldrin. The participants included 364 children aged two to seven, 446 parents of young children, and 149 older adults. The researchers found that average exposure levels of the children and adults exceeded cancer-benchmark levels for arsenic, as well as for lead, dieldrin, DDE, and dioxins. In children, arsenic (and dioxin) levels exceeded established cancer-benchmark levels 100-fold. The threat to the health of humans and animals is real, and we can identify some of the most common sources of contamination:

- *In water:* The standard for arsenic in drinking water is 10 parts per billion. That level is twice what the EPA proposed. Well water could possibly test even higher, depending on the proximity of industrial farming, glyphosate (Roundup), and chemical fertilizer applications in surrounding neighborhoods. Proximity to coal mines and other mining operations can also increase contamination of water, as can the sewage sludge (biosolids) frequently used as fertilizer.

- *In fruit:* The organic form of arsenic can be found in some fruits, at very, very low levels, but inorganic arsenic levels can be high in apple juice and orange juice. This is because apple concentrate that is often used to make apple juice is commonly imported from China, where arsenic is still used in pesticides. Likewise, orange juice can be made with "flavor packs" that are oils from the orange peel, often from Brazil, where a specific arsenic-containing fungicide is used. For now, it's a good idea to buy apple juice and orange juice from fruits grown in the U.S.

- *In animal feed:* Inorganic arsenic is commonly used in animal feed to make hogs and chickens grow faster. This inorganic arsenic is not only in the animals, but also the manure, which if spread on soil will ultimately and significantly raise the inorganic arsenic levels in ground used for growing food. Maryland is one of the first states to ban inorganic arsenic for poultry farms. Monosodium methyl arsenate (MSMA) is an arsenic herbicide compound sometimes applied to Bermuda grass pastures and hay. The EPA has recently stated that MSMA and other arsenic herbicides are ineligible for re-registration (except for use on cotton). However, residue from arsenic herbicide application can remain in soil and leach into streams.

Detox: Getting heavy metals out of the system

In recent years, I've had an increasing number of people tell me that their horse has tested high in arsenic based on hair analysis. Hair analysis is a useful tool, but it doesn't tell owners what is happening *now* in the horse's body, only what has already occurred at some point. If your horse's hair test shows high levels of one or more metal toxins, it is a good idea to get a blood test to confirm the presence of any toxins currently present in the body. If your horse or dog has tested high for arsenic or heavy metals (cadmium, lead, mercury, uranium) there are substances that can help the body gradually eliminate these toxins in a gentle fashion:

- **Calcium bentonite clay**: Due to its properties of adsorbtion (binding chemicals to its surface), this clay can remove toxins with its negative electrical charge.
- **Bladderwrack**: This brown sea vegetable provides alginate, which helps bind heavy metals.
- **Green and blue-green algae (*Chlorella, Spirulina*)**: These organisms bind heavy metals and increase available oxygen.

More food for thought

Research published in 2013 in the journal *Entropy* pinpoints the role of glyphosate in the suppression of cytochrome P450 (or "CYP") enzymes. These specialized proteins play a crucial role in detoxification of xenobiotics (chemicals not normally produced or expected to be present in an organism). The suppression of these enzymes, according to the research, enhances the damaging effects of chemical residues and environmental toxins, increasing inflammation, which damages cellular systems throughout the body and causes a disruption of the biosynthesis of amino acids by gut bacteria. If a dog, horse or human is eating food with GMO ingredients, it is possible that the body is unable to disarm other toxins like inorganic arsenic, heavy metals, or other chemical toxins because of the role that residual glyphosate can play in the suppression of P450/CYP enzymes. We'll find out more about the crucial role of enzymes in the next section on nutritionism.

While the sources and biological effects of toxic contaminants in the environment can be complicated, the trends have become all too clear. Our horses, dogs and cats are facing greater health challenges than ever before, as are our friends and family members. Cancer is the number one killer of dogs, and is on the rise in equines. Metabolic disease is now common in dogs, horses, and humans. Kidney disease in dogs and cats is escalating. Allergies in humans, dogs, cats, horses are nearing epidemic levels. On a list of leading causes of premature death in the U.S., Alzheimer's disease has skyrocketed from a ranking of 32nd in 1990 to a ranking of 9th in 2010—*a 392-percent increase.*

The further one goes down the Big Food (and Big Feed) research rabbit hole, the harder it can get to find much good health news. But again, the important thing is to remember we're not powerless against the environmental toxins making their way into food and feed, commercially processed or otherwise. Being proactive and minimizing their ill effects starts with being aware and following some core guidelines:

- If you are feeding your horses or pets food with GMOs, or if you are eating GMO food yourself, you might want to consider alternative food sources, like organics or "GMO-free"-labeled foods.

- Do not use glyphosate (Roundup), and avoid chemical fertilizers for lawns and pastures.
- If you are on a well, have your water tested yearly.
- If you are buying a feed with rice bran, or use rice bran as a supplement, verify the state of origin where the rice was grown. You have the right to request a certificate providing this information.
- If you feed rice to your dogs, either in a commercial food, or whole grain you cook at home, check with the company and get verification of state of origin.
- Avoid oranges grown in Brazil unless they are organic or pesticide/herbicide free. Avoid apple concentrate from China.
- Have your hay tested, and talk to your dealer about glyphosate-free hay.
- Support the microbiome of the GI tract with active probiotics.
- You can support the liver with herbs such as dandelion and milk thistle, and with medicinal mushrooms if you are concerned about toxins in your horse's environment.

APPENDIX C

Shampoos: A Chemical Soup

Equine and dog shampoos are as much a staple in barns and homes as food and grooming tools. The question that kept coming up for me was, what's really in these shampoos? So I decided to hop down the rabbit hole and find out.

I collected a list of ingredients of the top selling equine and canine shampoos, went to several tack stores, wrote down ingredients of lesser known brands, and started correlating the various chemicals. As I began my research into these various chemical concoctions, I was hit by the sudden realization that the skin is the largest organ of the microbiome, and we are stressing it with some powerful endocrine disruptors, carcinogens, and contact allergens. Some of these common chemical ingredients, when combined with other ingredients, become even more potentially toxic to the beneficial skin microorganisms, and to the bloodstream as well. Some are environmental hazards, affecting ground water and soil if they wash into fields and streams.

The more I studied the chemical components of shampoos, the more I began to focus on the correlation and connection of healthy gut and healthy skin. How are horses being affected by routine exposure? How are these chemicals affecting healthy populations of microorganisms in the skin? Since none of us usually bathe our horses and dogs with latex gloves, how are these chemicals in the shampoos affecting our skin and bloodstream? There are also, of course, the environmental impacts, such as having these chemicals washing into our groundwater and soils, ultimately to be taken up by grasses in our pastures.

Red flag ingredients

Methylparaben and *propylparaben*
Quickly absorbed through the skin, these preservatives have attracted a great deal of controversy with many reports of serious side effects. These compounds have been found intact within breast cancer tissues. They have been found to mimic estrogen and act as potential endocrine (hormone) disruptors.

Methylchloroisothiazolinone and *methylisothiazolinone*
Nearly impossible to pronounce, these preservatives (known as MCI/MIT) have been shown to induce skin sensitization in humans. The North American Contact Dermatitis Group named these preservatives "Contact Allergen of the Year" in 2013. In addition, research on rat brain cells found that brief exposure is highly toxic to cultured neurons.

Propylene glycol
Propylene glycol is a petroleum derivative found in products such as antifreeze and brake fluid as well as some lipsticks, toothpaste, and deodorant sticks. It can form a seal over the skin, preventing the escape of water; this does not add moisture to the skin. Propylene glycol tends to sit on the surface of skin after rinsing, dissolving fats and oils that the skin needs to stay nourished.

Sodium lauryl sulfate and *sodium laureth sulfate*
Known as SLS and SLES, these are used in testing labs as the standard ingredient to irritate skin, and are mainly used to create aesthetically preferred suds. They are used commonly in car wash soaps, garage floor cleaners, and engine degreasers. Both SLS and SLES may cause potentially carcinogenic formations of nitrates and dioxins to form by reacting with other product ingredients. The gradual, cumulative effects of long-term, repeated exposures are a real concern.

Cocamide diethanolamine (cocamide DEA)
The International Agency for Research on Cancer lists this ingredient as possibly carcinogenic to humans. In 2012, California listed cocamide DEA under its Proposition 65 law which requires warning labels on consumer products containing carcinogens or reproductive toxicants.

Cocamidopropyl betaine (CAPB)
A well-documented contact allergen and contributor to dermatitis.

Hexyl cinnamal
This is a synthetic scent ingredient, currently on the EU list of banned and restricted fragrances as a possible human immune system toxicant or allergen, but found in equine shampoos in the U.S.

Polysorbate 80
There are two grades of this emulsifier: cosmetic grade and food grade. It is the cosmetic grade that is of most concern, as it may contain ethylene oxide and 1,4-dioxane, which have high hazard ratings.

Polysorbate 20
This is also an emulsifier that is treated with the carcinogenic ethylene oxide and can be contaminated with 1,4-dioxane. The Campaign for Safe Cosmetics reported that the levels in 1,4-dioxane found in personal care products are 1,000 times higher than those found to cause cancer in animal studies.

Triclosan and *triclocarban*
These two ingredients came under fire by the FDA as a result of research showing that they may aid the growth of antibiotic-resistant bacteria. Some experts have called these antibacterial chemicals a public health threat. New data point to triclosan and triclocarban as having endocrine-disrupting potential as well.

Tetrasodium EDTA
This is a preservative made from formaldehyde and sodium cyanide. Some animal studies have found this chelating agent to have reproductive effects because it can bind with minerals. It is slow to degrade, making it a poor choice for environmental health.

For all we do for our horses and dogs in terms of choosing food and supplements, I feel that not addressing the toxic ingredients in equine and canine shampoos would be a mistake. These chemicals can degrade the microbiome of the skin, potentially enter the bloodstream, and contribute to environmental damage at our farms and homes.

APPENDIX D

The Benefits of Beer

Guinness Stout beer is often recommended as an aid to help horses with anhidrosis, but beer for horses goes beyond that. On the backside of many race tracks across the country and in the barns of many well-known show jumpers, Guinness Stout is a regular part of supplementing a horse's diet.

At the Winter Equestrian Festival in Wellington, Florida, I was amazed at how much beer sat in feed rooms waiting to be fed. For show jumpers, Guinness is being fed after competitions to revitalize the horses. On the track, Guinness helps to stimulate appetite in picky eaters. One thoroughbred trainer at the Saratoga track said, "although it's more expensive to use Guinness, if you feed cheap beer it gives the horses a hangover."

Components of Guinness Stout

Guinness is made from the yeast *Saccharomyces cervisiae*, which is often found as a probiotic in feed and supplements. In addition to probiotic support, yeast provides much of the B-vitamin complex (an important nutritional component in helping horses recover from stress).

In addition, Guinness contains hops. Hops became an important herbal component in beer-making beginning in the 13th century when English monks (who had a monopoly on beer-making) discovered the antimicrobial actions of the hops flower that grows in marshy hollows all over Europe. In Traditional Chinese Medicine, hops are used as a digestive aid, and as a treatment for dysentery. The ancient Greek and Roman physicians also recommended hops for intestinal ailments. Recently, French researchers have identified that hops appears to relax the smooth lining of the digestive tract in humans. The phytochemicals in hops include quercetin, a powerful anti-inflammatory, antioxidant and rho iso-alpha acid (RIAA) that has been shown to modulate insulin signaling and decrease the deleterious effects of lipotoxicity in vitro and in a human clinical trial on patients with metabolic syndrome.

Guinness beer also contains malted barley, produced from whole barley grain. Malted barley is a good source of B-vitamins and the minerals iron, copper, manganese and selenium. Iron and copper help make more red blood cells, which can increase the oxygen carrying capacity of the blood. Manganese and selenium are powerful antioxidants, helping to protect cells and tissues from superoxide free radicals.

Last but not least among reasons to consider beer for horses, is the component of water in Guinness beer. The water comes from springs in the Wicklow Mountains in Ireland. It's important to note that Guinness is brewed in Ireland and then imported to the U.S. It is not made by a licensed brewery in the U.S., as are some other imported beers.

Recommended feeding of beer for horses

- High-performance horses: 12 oz. (one bottle) once per day.
- Horses in moderate work/training: ½ cup once per day.

- Guinness can be fed as needed after a hard training session, after a competition, or during a period of high heat and/or high humidity.

I also feed ½ cup per day to the retired horses, when temperatures hit the 90-degree mark, and I swear I see a smile on their lips after they finish their feed.

APPENDIX E

The Rise of Western Medicine in the U.S.

It was while I was reading *The History, Treatment, and Diseases of the Horse* (1880 edition) that I came upon the chapter titled, "List of the medicines used in the treatment of the diseases of the horse." Some of the treatments like purging and blood-letting were a bit hard to read, but the medicines of that time were fascinating: lots of homeopathic preparations, and then some "cures" like mercury and lead which were a little frightening, but the one that grabbed my attention was opium.

> *It is obtained by making incisions into the unripe capsule of the poppy and scraping the juice which exhales, and drying it in the sun. The best kind of opium is brought to this country in chests from Turkey and India...it is a powerful antispasmodic, sedative, and astringent. As an antispasmodic it enters into the colic drink, and it is the sheet-anchor of the veterinarian in the treatment of locked-jaw and tetanus...it becomes an excellent tonic because it is a sedative.*

It started me thinking...about the opioid problem we have currently in the U.S., from heroin to morphine, hydrocodone, oxycodone, codeine and fentanyl. So I did a little research.

Opium was cultivated in lower Mesopotamia around 3400 BC. The Sumerians passed it along to the Assyrians, who then passed it to the Egyptians. The opium trade flourished during the reigns of Thutmose IV, Akhenaton and Tutankhamen. This trade route included the Phoenicians and Minoans, who brought opium to Greece, Carthage and Europe. Around 460 BC, Hippocrates, the father of medicine, acknowledge its usefulness as a narcotic and styptic in treating internal diseases and diseases of women. Opium from Thebes was introduced to China by Arab traders in 400 AD. During the 1300s opium disappears from Europe for 200 hundred years because of the taboo put on it by the Holy Inquisition who considered anything from the East as being linked to the devil.

In 1527, opium was reintroduced into European medical literature as "laudanum". It was the Dutch in 1700 who introduced the practice of smoking opium in a pipe to the Chinese. The British East India Company, in 1793, established a monopoly on the opium trade, and the company's import of opium into China reached a staggering 2,000 chests per year. In 1803, Friedrich Sertuerner of Germany discovered the active ingredient in opium by dissolving it in acid and then neutralizing it with ammonia. The result was morphine. In 1827, E. Merck & Company of Darmstadt, Germany began the commercial manufacturing of morphine. It would become a dominant manufacturer of morphine, codeine and cocaine. In 1895, Heinrich Dreser working for the Bayer Company of Elberfeld, Germany found that diluting morphine with acetyls produced a drug without the common morphine side effects. Bayer began production of diacetylmorphine and coined the name for this new compound: heroin.

Further down the rabbit hole: J.D. Rockefeller

When I think of Bayer, I think of aspirin, not heroin. I was curious about the use of acetyls to produce heroin. Where did the acetyls come from in the late 1800s? Well, just like today they come from petrochemicals, which then led me to John D. Rockefeller, the oil baron. In the late 1800s, Rockefeller came up with an idea to use coal tar, a petroleum derivative, to make substances that affect the body and nervous system. This was not a new idea; his father Old Bill Rockefeller sold bottles of raw petroleum mixed with a little opium as a cure for cancer. Young Rockefeller just needed a vehicle to extend and capitalize on petroleum derivatives as medicines.

The rise of the American Medical Association

In the early 1900's there were many types of healing practices in the U.S. and Europe: chiropractors, naturopathy, midwives, homeopathy, osteopathy, herbal medicines, diet, and steam baths. Western medicine in the 18th and 19th centuries was called Heroic Medicine and included methods such as blood-letting, purging, leeching, blistering, mercury and lead therapy.

Through much of history, healers were those who worked with herbs and food, and charged little or nothing for their expertise. The rise of heroic medicine brought about the idea of healing as a job. Heroic medicine practitioners charged more money for treatments than traditional healers. In many places only the wealthy class could afford a doctor of heroic medicine. Because heroic medicine treatment was so often unpleasant and even lethal, more of the populace chose the milder treatments of the herbalists. Thomas Jefferson called heroic medicine physicians an "inexperienced and presumptuous band of medical tyros let loose upon the world."

The underpinnings that created the American Medical Association (AMA) were based on a strategy to enhance the medical profession's position in society. According to Richard E. Brown, author of Rockefeller Medicine Men: Medicine and Capitalism in America, "Scientific medicine gained the support of the medical profession in the late nineteenth century because it met the economic and social needs of physicians."

The AMA began in 1847, but it was a small, weak organization until John D. Rockefeller and Andrew Carnegie took on a "philanthropic mission" to help it grow, marking the point when allopathic (Western) medicine took a huge turn. Since there were many types of doctors and healing methods, Rockefeller wanted to eliminate these competitors, thus ensuring that drugs would be the main course of treatment. Capitalists like Rockefeller and Carnegie and others "embraced scientific medicine as an ideological weapon in their struggle to formulate a new culture appropriate to and supportive of industrial capitalism."

Rockefeller and Carnegie hired Abraham Flexner, an American educator, to write a report, published and given to Congress in 1910, that concluded there were too many doctors and medical schools in the U.S., and that all natural healing modalities which had existed for hundreds of years were unscientific quackery. Flexner's report called for standardization of medical education, whereby only allopathic AMA medicine institutions would be granted medical school licenses. Congress acted on the conclusions and made them law. Carnegie and Rockefeller used their tax-exempt foundations to offer huge grants to medical schools on the proviso that only an allopathic curriculum be taught. Curricula in these schools was dismantled to remove herbs and plants, and the importance of diet. On the positive side, Flexner's influence did heighten the importance of laboratory-based research and education.

The rise of science: Allopathic medicine

From heroic medicine arose scientific medicine, so called because it replaced healing as art, and represented a method of practice "not based on dogma but on verifiable truths." Scientific medicine focused on disease as an engineering problem. "The technical expertise associated with scientific medicine helps to mystify the role and work of the physician more effectively...thereby support[ing] the claims of the profession for a monopoly of control over all healing methods."

Scientific medicine made physicians more dependent on capital-intensive commodities, especially drugs, which were the essential base of their practices. Prescription drugs gave doctors new power by forcing the public to see a physician in order to obtain the benefits of medical research.

Mainstream Western medicine is sometimes referred to as "allopathic medicine". The term "allopathy" refers to the practice of healing through opposites. If the patient is retaining water, then a drug that promotes urination is the answer. The term "homeopathy" is derived from the Greek *homoios*, which means "similar" and *pathos*, which means "suffering". Homeopathic means "like cures like."

The Rockefellers and their pharmaceutical empire

With the AMA and allopathic medical schools firmly in place, the abolition of other medicinal therapies, and the enforcement of regulated licensing of doctors, the Rockefeller empire continued to expand. Sterling Drug Inc. (the largest holding company in the Rockefeller drug empire) and its 68 subsidiaries were maintained under an umbrella with the Rockefeller-owned bank Chase Manhattan (now known as J.P. Morgan Chase Bank) and called the Drug Trust.

Under the directive of the Rockefeller Foundation, funds to medical colleges in 1948 alone swelled to $32 million, which in today's money would amount to $323 million. This ensured that the medical schools would teach and indoctrinate with the names and uses of thousands of drugs. We cannot forget that the pharmaceutical empire of the Rockefellers includes vaccines, sedatives, analgesics, antibiotics, heart drugs, and hypnotics.

In the 1930's John D. Rockefeller, Jr. campaigned for the prohibition of hemp and cannabis through generous political and Baptist church donations. Hemp could produce ethanol, which competed with petroleum, and cannabis was a competitor with opium and with the Rockefeller-owned member of an opium cartel: Bayer, creators of heroin.

John D. Rockefeller purchased shares in what was to become a massive German chemical and pharmaceutical cartel; I.G. Farben was a conglomerate of several big chemical manufacturers including Bayer, Hoechst, and BASF. This conglomerate would invent, produce and distribute the Zyklon B used in Nazi concentration camps, producing enough of the gas to kill 200 million humans. In 1939, I.G. Farben purchased $20 million worth of high-grade aviation gasoline from Standard Oil of New Jersey, owned by Rockefeller. That same year, a new company was formed with Standard Oil taking 15 percent of the stock to protect Germany's holdings in chemicals and drugs. This new company was called The American I.G. Farben.

Side note: Auschwitz was actually built by I.G. Farben. Before it became an extermination camp, it was the largest industrial complex known in Europe. Farber executives were among those found guilty of war crimes and served prison terms after the war.

Before the attack on Pearl Harbor, American I.G. Farben purchased an undisclosed number of shares in several companies: Schering, Monsanto Chemical, Dow Chemical, and DuPont. It also took over the privately owned Hoffman-Laroche Company (who would become one of the largest producers of coal tar vitamins in the world).

Morris A. Bealle and the Rockefeller Drug Trust

In the 1930s, Morris Bealle, a former city editor of the *Washington Times and Herald* started his own paper in one of the local Maryland counties. The local power company bought a large ad every week, but when Bealle wrote an editorial about the poor service the power company had given some of the paper's readers, Bealle was hauled in front of the advertising agency and told that if he stepped out of line again, it would result in the immediate cancellation of the advertising contract as well as contracts with the gas and telephone companies.

To Bealle, this was not the meaning of a free press. He closed the newspaper and started investigating incidents of infringement of the free press, which led him to the Rockefellers. Unable to get his exposés printed through existing channels, he established his own publishing company, The Columbia Publishing House, in 1949. His book, *The Drug*

Story; A Factological History of America's Drug Cartel was published in 1949, and remains one of the definitive accounts of the wealth, power, and control wielded by the Rockefeller Drug Trust.

In his book, Bealle illuminates the links between Rockefeller power and government. "This Bureau—now known as the Food and Drug Administration—is used primarily for the perversion of justice by cracking down on all who endanger the profits of the Drug Trust." Bealle further points out that the FDA is "very assiduous in putting out of business any and all vendors of therapeutic devices which increase the health incidence of the public and thus decrease the profit incidence of the Drug Trust."

Dr. Adolphus Hohensee

This doctor was known as one of America's leading vitaminologists (a term I have only found in use in the 1930s-1940s). He gave advice on diet and sold vitamin supplements such as B-complex, lecithin, and wheat germ oil, stating that the soil was depleted of nutrients and that foods were over-processed. In 1945, the FDA prosecuted him for misbranding based on the testimony of ten AMA experts who claimed that "vitamins are not necessary to the human body" and that dietary deficiency diseases did not exist, as they had been eradicated in America with fortified foods. Dr. Hohensee was found guilty and fined $1,800 (approximately $23,000 today).

Sulfathiazole

In 1940, a new drug called sulfathiazole was created by Winthrop Drug Company, a subsidiary of the Drug Trust, and approved by J.J. Durrett, a Rockefeller appointee to the FDA.

That December, four hundred thousand sulfathiazole tablets were released on the market. These tablets were a mixture of sulfa drug and phenobarbital. Although the standard safe dosage for phenobarbital in 1940 was one grain, many of the sulfathiazole tablets released contained as much as five grains. Three hundred deaths were directly linked to sulfathiazole. No one from Winthrop Drug was held accountable.

Allopathic medicine today

There is no question that there are medicines which are life-saving for both humans and animals. There are important drug therapies that are important in human and animal medicine. Advances in the treatment of various diseases have been enormous. Thirty years ago, many veterinarians viewed chiropractics, massage, herbs, traditional Chinese medicine, and acupuncture as akin to "selling snake oil." How that has changed! Now those complementary medicines and therapies are widely accepted and recommended. Many veterinarian and allopathic doctors have opened their minds and embraced a more whole approach to healing.

But the dark side of allopathic medicine remains: the constant bombardment of practitioners and consumers with drugs and vaccines, some of which function mainly to increase the pharmaceutical cartel's profits.

According to an article published by the Edmond J. Safra Center for Ethics at Harvard University, "prescription drugs [are] a major health risk, ranking 4th with stroke as a leading cause of death" (Donald W. Light, 2014). A study funded by the National Institute on Aging and published online in the journal Mayo Clinic Proceedings (2013) claimed that nearly 70% of Americans are on at least one prescription drug and more than 50% take two. Antibiotics, antidepressants, and opioids are the most commonly prescribed. According to a report by the Federal Trade Commission (2015) companion animal medication sales (including prescription and over-the-counter) reached $7.6 billion dollars in 2013 and is expected to grow to $10.2 billion by 2018. Unfortunately, I could find no similar data on equine medications.

Full circle: Back to opioids and the Rockefellers

I started down this rabbit hole to learn more about opium based on its use as a sedative in 19th-century veterinary medicine. It is still in veterinary use today, although in a synthetic form called butorphanol tartrate (trade name Torbugesic). Torbugesic is owned by Wyeth, who is owned by Pfizer. On the board of Pfizer are two directors from Exxon Mobil. Exxon is the former Standard Oil Company, which split into different companies such as Standard Oil of New Jersey and Standard Oil Company of New York, once called Socony and in 1920 renamed Mobil. Exxon and Mobil have always been a part of the Rockefeller dynasty. Two other members of the Pfizer board are directors of J.P. Morgan Chase Bank—the original home of the Rockefeller Drug Trust.

Of course, most opioid use is by humans, specifically Americans. A 2012 study showed that US residents consumed 80% of the opioid drugs produced in the world, and 99% of the world's hydrocodone.

Vitamins and petroleum

Most processed foods, feeds, and supplements are fortified with coal-tar and petroleum-derived nutrients. When it comes to these synthetic vitamins and nutraceuticals, we are led once again to the petroleum industry, the Rockefellers, and the drug trust; In 2002, Hoffman Larouche, one of the largest producers of vitamins and part of the drug trust owned by the Rockefellers, was sold to Dutch conglomerate DSM for $2.24 billion.

Healing in the 21st century

With the skyrocketing costs of important drugs and the obscene greed that has been exhibited by companies like Mylan Pharmaceuticals with their EpiPen price increase, and Turing Pharmaceuticals' mind-blowing increase on their AIDS drug from $13.50 per pill to $750, it's no wonder many of us are pondering what the future of pharmaceuticals is going to look like. Human cancer treatment drugs have gone from $10,000 in 2000 to $100,000 or more in 2015. Even generic drug prices have doubled, tripled. A good example is the antibiotic doxyclycline (100 miligrams), which soared from $20 for 500 capsules in 2013 to $1,849 in 2014.

Food, water, and environment make up the foundation of health. The choices we make on what to eat, and what to feed our horses and dogs are among the most vital and critical health choices we can make. We have available so many complimentary medicines and therapies: traditional Chinese medicine (TCM), Ayurveda, western herbalism, homeopathy, massage, acupuncture, chiropractics, and the newer modalities such as ultrasound therapy, vibration therapy, laser therapy, magnetic and ceramic therapy.

We have other options. We can approach healing as a dynamic, fluid whole rather than as a single paradigm.

APPENDIX F

Ayurveda: The Oldest Medicine on Earth

My first exposure to Ayurveda was in 1984 at The Natural Products Expo in Atlanta. I was working for a (human) nutritional supplement company that sold products through independent health food stores. Standing in the trade booth on the first day of the expo, I saw two Sikhs walking by. My eyes followed them to a booth at the end of the aisle. On a break, my curiosity propelled me toward that booth. Spread out on the table were packages of small yellow beans, and herbs that I had never heard of: *amalaki, guggulu, dashamula, boswellia, ashoka.*

"What is this?" I asked politely.

"These are some of the medicines of Ayurveda," one of the Sikhs said softly.

I had no idea what "Ayurveda" meant. I had never heard the word before. A few Chinese herbs from TCM (traditional Chinese medicine) had inched into the health food business in the early 1980's: herbs such as ginseng, ma huang, astragalus, and ginger. In complete ignorance I said, "Are these new Chinese herbs?"

"The medicine of Ayurveda is older than that," the other Sikh said. "It is the oldest medicine on earth."

The ancient philosophy of Ayurveda is so named for "life knowledge": *ayur* means life, and *veda* means knowledge. It arose in India thousands of years ago. The great seers of India came to understand and reveal the deepest truths of human physiology and health through deep meditation and spiritual practices. These truths and practices were passed down orally until they were compiled and organized into an elaborate system of sacred texts recorded in the Vedas—the world's oldest existing literature, written in Sanskrit more than 5,000 years ago. By 400 AD, the Ayurvedic texts had been translated into Chinese, and by 700 AD Chinese scholars were studying Ayurveda in India. Among many other topics, these texts include information on the care, health management, and disease treatment of the animals.

Balance of mind, body, spirit

The fundamental root of Ayurveda is the idea that *health is the balanced and dynamic integration of environment, body, mind, and spirit.* In Ayurveda, it is all connected.

There are five elements in Ayurveda: space, air, fire, water, and earth. The term "space" refers to what was once called "ether", and in the ancient philosophies was thought to be prevalent in the heavens but inaccessible to humans.

There are three basic energies that govern the inner and outer environments of *movement, transformation,* and *structure.* These energies are derived from the five elements and are referred to as *doshas.* When a dosha becomes out of balance, various mental and physical conditions can result.

Dosha	Elements	Associations	Imbalance indicators
Vata	air, space	nervous system, bodily movements	anxiety, dry skin, constipation, difficulty focusing
Pitta	fire, water	metabolism, digestion, vision	indigestion, ulcers, inflammation, skin rashes, diarrhea
Kapha	earth, water	structure, lubrication, stability	weight gain, sluggishness, indigestion, slow or suppressed metabolism, lymphatic congestion, prediabetes

There are times when more than one dosha can be out of balance, as in the case of an overweight horse with gastric ulcers. This would indicate an imbalance of both the Pitta dosha and Kapha dosha.

Cooling, warming, neutral

Similar to traditional Chinese medicine, Ayurveda focuses on foods, herbs, plants, and spices that are categorized as cooling, warming, or neutral. For example, a horse with gastric ulcers would be seen as having an imbalance of the Pitta dosha. Since

Pitta is derived from fire, an ulcer would signify too much fire in the GI tract. The Ayurvedic approach would be to support the horse with foods such as *Lactobacillus acidophilus,* a probiotic bacteria from milk, which is cooling. A yeast probiotic would not be recommended because active yeast is warming; if we already have too much fire in the GI tract, we don't need to add more heat.

Examples of neutral foods include almonds and hemp seeds.

Tridoshic foods for horses

These are foods and plants that are *tridoshic*—that is, balancing for all three doshas: pumpkin seeds, sunflower seeds, sesame seeds, chia, flax, almonds, coconut (in small amounts), blueberries, pomegranate, alfalfa, cabbage, kale, seaweeds, quinoa, rice (in moderation), ashwaganda, holy basil, black pepper, amla (Indian Gooseberry), turmeric, oregano, mung beans, mung dal (split yellow beans), fennel, parsley, carrots, dandelions, squash, the green algae chlorella, and the blue-green algae spirulina.

The Ayurvedic influence

From the moment I met the Sikhs at that Natural Products Expo many years ago, I was drawn like a magnet to Ayurveda. The philosophy of balancing the whole body system rather than pieces of the body system resonated with me. This would be in conflict with the Western (allopathic) nutrition training I had, until I learned how to use both Ayurveda and Western nutritionism together. In the past 30 years, more scientific research has been conducted on various plants used widely in Ayurveda, and studies have proven the wisdom in the old

Ayurvedic Sanskrit texts. Although the ancients didn't have the same methodology, they did in fact have a profound understanding of the relationship between food, plants, environment, and health.

AFTERWORD - What Horses Used to Eat: Feeding Horses in 1858

A veterinary surgeon named John Stewart, professor of veterinary medicine in Glasgow, Scotland, wrote a book that was published in 1858 called *The Stable Book: Being a Treatise on the Management of Horses.* With regard to what we know about feeding horses today, it's fascinating to do a little compare-and-contrast with Stewart's observations. Readers in the twenty-first century might chuckle at the frequent mentions of *draughts* and *cordials* for horses (according to Dr. Stewart, a cordial helps many an ill or over-worked horse), *tonic balls* (an herbal preparation made into a ball with honey that is fed orally) and a *physic* (herbs and other concoctions directed by a veterinarian). *Blood-letting* is mentioned as treatment for some disorders. But the real focus of the book is *feeding* horses.

It's quite surprising to read about some of the items used for feeding horses in the 19th century: turnips, potatoes, parsnips, sugar beets, mangel-wurzel (another beet), carrots, and yams. These root vegetables are all boiled or steamed before feeding, with the exception of the carrot, and mostly fed in winter. "A work horse getting from between eight to twelve pounds of grain," says Stewart, "may have four pounds deducted for every five pounds of carrots he receives." The author recommends turnips for farm and cart horses, and for horses in coaching stables. He specifically recommends the Swedish variety of turnips, stating that "100 pounds of Swedes are equal in nutriment to 22 of hay." As a modern-day horse owner, it's hard to imagine feeding 100 pounds of turnips per day.

Wheaten bread (recommended for horses that are invalid or off their appetite), linseed, hempseed, oats, barley, and beans were commonly fed to horses in the mid-19th century. Stewart does not recommend bran, except for a horse that is off his feed, explaining that bran "contains little nutriment...A shilling's worth of oats is a great deal more nourishing than a shilling's worth of bran."

Stewart provides a travelogue of diets used for feeding horses in different countries: pumpkins, apples, sweet potatoes, and corn stalks in America; figs and chestnuts in Spain and Italy; dates mixed with camel's milk in Arabia; dried fish in Iceland and Norway; black bread, rye, malt, and rye bread in Germany and Holland. In the East Indies, he describes "meat boiled to rags, to which is added some kinds of grain and butter," and "sheep's heads...boiled for horses" during military campaigns in India. In England, cows' milk was given to stallions during the "covering season," while horses living near the sea could be fed dried and ground seaweed.

The book also provides various feeding schedules based on the type of horse: cart, carriage, hunter, cavalry, racehorse, and saddle horse. For most horses, Stewart recommends feeding five times per day—at 6 a.m., 9 a.m., 1 p.m., 5 p.m., and 8 p.m.—with a total consumption of 12 to 16 pounds of grain (oats and beans) with 12 pounds of hay. In winter, he recommends feeding boiled food for the last meal of the day, with added turnips, while carrots should be given raw throughout the day. For horses in "laborious" work, he recommends adding barley, with the ratio then being 6:3:3 (oats to beans to barley), plus hay.

Although Stewart explains how important pasture is for young growing horses, he is strongly against daily turn out for working horses because of "weight gain and a tendency to laziness." He does recommend that, one day per week, horses get pasture time, particularly access to hedgerows of various plants. He also suggests feeding native herbs like dandelion leaf, hawthorn, milk thistle, mint, and marshmallow root.

Not recommended are distillery grains or brewers grains, which Stewart calls "the refuse of breweries." He claims that, when fed regularly, "they produce general rottenness, which I suspect in this case means disease of the liver. They are also blamed for producing staggers and founder." Dr. Stewart cautions against raw wheat as well, because "fermentation, colic and death are the consequences"; however, he says that if wheat is boiled and given with beans, oats, and chaff, that it "can be useful."

It is clear from reading *The Stable Book* that feeding horses in 1858 largely depended on what food was available, which varied from country to country. And while we may think of horses in the 19th century as living bucolic lives, in truth these horses worked daily, worked hard, and had limited access to pasture because they worked six days a week, either carrying riders, pulling coaches, carts, plows, and wagons, or galloping into battle. The amount of feed required for a working horse in the 19th century vastly outweighs the feed requirements of most present day sport horses.

We do know a lot more about the nutritional needs of horses than horsemen did in the 1800s. Yet, there are important insights to be gained from understanding what feeding horses used to entail:

- From turnips to oats, horses were fed whole food—not turnip skins or turnip flour, not oat hulls or oat protein powder. Feeding whole, real food makes a whole, real difference.

- It's interesting that, in 1858, a veterinarian would caution against the use of things like distillery grains and uncooked wheat. We see these same ingredients today in many commercial horse feeds and supplements as "dried distillers grains" or "dried distillers grains with solubles," or "wheat middlings." The distillers grains now used in animal feeds are the byproduct of the ethanol industry and are made from corn. Some feed companies have removed dried distillers grains because they are a potential source of *mycotoxins*. The other concern is the antibiotics used on the corn mash for ethanol production. In 2009, the FDA tested 27 samples of dried distillers grains and found antibiotic residue in 17 of them.

- Dr. Stewart's recommendation of frequent feedings is a good reminder today for those horses that are primarily stabled with limited turnout. Smaller amounts of food, fed more often, is the best feed plan for the health of the equine GI tract.

- For hardworking horses of the 19th century, significant amounts of carbohydrate, fat, protein, and fiber foods were required to replace the calories burned and provide the energy to work for 8 to 10 hours per day. Most horses today don't have such high caloric needs.

Acknowledgements

Thank you to the horses that have educated me far better than academia, and to their riders and owners and trainers and veterinarians who have the courage to try a different approach.

Thank you to *Bernie McMahon* for being a shelter in the storm, and for your wisdom and guidance and trust. There would be no BioStar without you.

Thank you to my partner *Peter* for stepping to the beat of a different drum with me.

Thank you to the canine crew: *Kemosabe, Thunderbear, Buckaroo, Crockett,* and *Yoda*. Your paw prints on my heart can never be wiped away.

A special thanks to the team in Gordonsville, Virginia: *Rick, Lynn, Elva, Cindy, Jaime, JP, Lindsay, Judy,* and *Emily*; and to the satellite crew, *Leslie* and *Dave*. You are the wings I fly on.

Bibliography

Blaser, Martin J. *Missing Microbes: How the Overuse of Antibiotics Is Fueling Our Modern Plagues.* Henry Holt and Co., 2014

Brown, Richard E., *Rockefeller Medicine Men: Medicine and Capitalism in America.* University of California Press, 1981.

Campbell, T. Colin. *Whole: Rethinking the Science of Nutrition.* BenBella Books, 2013.

Chavkin, Sasha. "Mysterious Kidney Disease Now 'Top Priority' in Central America." International Consortium of Investigative Journalists, 29 Apr. 2013. Web. 04 Sept. 2016.

Costa, M.C., et al. "Comparison of the fecal microbiota of healthy horses and horses with colitis by high throughput sequencing of the V3-V5 region of the 16S rRNA gene." *PLoS One.* vol. 7, no. 7, 2012, www.ncbi.nlm.nih.gov/pubmed/22859989. Accessed 4 October, 2016.

Davis, William. *Wheat Belly: Lose the Wheat, Lose the Weight, and Find Your Path Back to Health.* Rodale Books, 2014.

"Ethoxyquin: Controversial Dog Food Additive."
DogFoodAdvisor, www.dogfoodadvisor.com/red-flag-
ingredients/ethoxyquin-dangerous-dog-food-additive.
Accessed 4 October, 2016.

"FDA Sampling Detects Antibiotic Residues in Ethanol
Distillers Products." NGFA Newsletter 61 (29 Jan. 2009):
n. pag. National Grain and Feed Association. Web. 6 Sept.
2016.

Flaws, Bob. *The Tao of Healthy Eating: Dietary Wisdom
According to Traditional Chinese Medicine*. Blue Poppy
Press, 1998.

Frawley, David and Vasant Lad. *The Yoga of Herbs: An
Ayurvedic Guide to Herbal Medicine*. Lotus Press, 1986.

Friedrich, M. J. "Genetic Damage Linked to Elevated Arsenic
Levels in Rice." Journal of the American Medical
Association 310.11 (2013): 1113. Web.

Frost, Robert. "The Road Not Taken." *The Atlantic Monthly*,
Aug. 1915.

Goldstein, Robert S., editor. *Integrating Complementary
Medicine into Veterinary Practice*. Wiley-Blackwell, 2008.

Institute for Health Metrics and Evaluation. "The State of US
Health: Innovations, Insights, and Recommendations from

the Global Burden of Disease Study." Seattle, WA: IHME, 2013.

Keeler, Barbara, and Marc Lappe. "Some Food for FDA Regulation." Los Angeles Times. Los Angeles Times, 2001. Web. 05 Sept. 2016.

Light, Donald W., "New Prescription Drugs: A Major Health Risk With Few Offsetting Advantages." 27 June, 2014. Harvard University Edmond J. Safra Center for Ethics. http://ethics.harvard.edu/blog/new-prescription-drugs-major-health-risk-few-offsetting-advantages. Accessed 4 October, 2016.

Minich, Deanna M., et al. "Hop and Acacia Phytochemicals Decreased Lipotoxicity in 3T3-L1 Adipocytes, db/dbMice, and Individuals with Metabolic Syndrome." *Journal of Nutrition and Metabolism*, 18 May, 2010. Web.

Murray, Michael and Joseph Pizzorno. *The Encyclopedia of Natural Medicine*. Prima Publishing, 1991.

Passwater, Richard A. "Nutrition and Championship Sports Performance, Recovery and Injury Reduction: A Major Role for Cherry Juice Beyond Arthritis Relief (An Interview with Malachy McHugh, Ph.D.)." *Whole Foods Magazine* Oct. 2010: n. pag. Web. 05 Sept. 2016.

Perlmutter, David. *Brain Maker: The Power of Gut Microbes to Heal and Protect Your Brain—for Life*. Little, Brown and Company, 2015.

"Pet Food Labels - General." Pet Food Labels - General. U.S. Food and Drug Administration, n.d. Web. 04 Sept. 2016.

Pollan, Michael (2008). *In Defense of Food: An Eater's Manifesto*. New York, USA: Penguin Press.

Rai, Yash. *Holy Basil: Tulsi*. India: Naveet Publications, 2002.

Samsel, Anthony, and Stephanie Seneff. "Glyphosate's Suppression of Cytochrome P450 Enzymes and Amino Acid Biosynthesis by the Gut Microbiome: Pathways to Modern Diseases." Entropy 15.4 (2013): 1416-463. Web.

Schatzker, Mark. *The Dorito Effect: The Surprising New Truth About Food and Flavor*. N.p.: Simon & Schuster, 2015. Print.

Scrinis, Gyorgy (2013). *Nutritionism: The Science and Politics of Dietary Advice*. Columbia University Press. ISBN 9780231527149. Retrieved 15 April 2015.

Sjerven, Jay. "Antibiotics Use in Animals in the Spotlight | Food Business News." Sosland Publishing Company, 25 Apr. 2012. Web. 04 Sept. 2016.

Stewart, John. *The Stable Book: Being a Treatise on the Management of Horses*. N.p.: BiblioLife, 2009. Print.

Szent-Gyorgyi, "Oxidation, energy transfer, and vitamins." A. Lindsten, Jan, editor. *Nobel Lectures: Physiology or Medicine, 1922-1941*. World Scientific, 1999.

Takahashi, I., and H. Kiyono. "Gut as the Largest Immunologic Tissue." *Journal of Parenteral and Enteral Nutrition*. 23.5 Suppl. Sept.-Oct., 1999.

"Tetracyclines: Anti-bacterial Agents." Merck Sharp & Dohme Corp., Nov. 2015. Web. 05 Sept. 2016.

Thomas F., Hehemann J.H., et al. "Environmental and Gut Bacteroidetes: The Food Connection." *Frontiers in Microbiology*. 2011; 2-93.

Vogt, R., et al. "Cancer and Non-cancer Health Effects from Food Contaminant Exposures for Children and Adults in California: A Risk Assessment." *Environmental Health*. 11.1 (2012).

Warner, Melanie. *Pandora's Lunchbox: How Processed Food Took Over the American Meal*. First Scribner hardcover edition. Scribner, 2013.

Youatt, William. *The History, Treatment and Diseases of the Horse*, for the Society for the Diffusion of Useful Knowledge. Hartford: S. Andrus & Son, 1853.

Zawadzki MK, et al. "Carbohydrate-protein Complex Increases the Rate of Muscle Glycogen Storage after Exercise." *Journal of Applied Physiology* 72.5 (1992): 1854-859. Web.

About the Author

Tigger Montague has spent most of her life with horses. From riding ponies as a child, to training and competing in eventing and dressage as an adult, and even letting her inner cowgirl out on ranch vacations, her passion for horses and animals has been a lifelong dedication. With over 30 years in the nutrition business both human and equine, she has combined her experience with her love of exploring "the rabbit hole": deep investigation of both the science and the philosophies of food and nutrition. Her company, BioStarUS, has pioneered the formulation and production of whole, non-GMO, raw food supplements for horses and dogs.

CPSIA information can be obtained
at www.ICGtesting.com
Printed in the USA
BVHW070158311220
596738BV00007B/638

9 781634 919067